Mythology

Teacher Edition

Written by Rebecca Stark

Cover Design by Susan Banta
Illustrations by Nelsy Fontalvo
and Karen Neulinger

Explanation of cover design: The symbol represents the Great Unity. According to Chinese mythology, out of the Great Unity there came the two opposing forces of Yin and Yang. Yin is the passive female element, force or principle. It is complementary to Yang, the active masculine principle.

ISBN: 1-56644-965-0 (Teacher Edition)

EDUCATIONAL IMPRESSIONS, INC.
Hawthorne, NJ 07507

Table of Contents

Introduction 4

What Is Mythology? 5-6
Mythology of the Ancient Greeks 7-26
   The Origin of the World 10
   Zeus and the Gods of Mt. Olympus 11
   Zeus's Brothers 12-13
   The Artist God 13
   A Foolhardy Request 14-15
   Interpreting the Will of the Gods 16
   The Judgment of Paris 17-19
   Lesser Divinities 20-26
      Prometheus and the Gift of Fire 21-23
      The Twelve Labours of Heracles 24
      Echo and Narcissus 25-26
Roman Mythology 27-30
   Protectors of the Household 28
   Minerva 29
   Cupid and Psyche 30
Norse and Germanic Mythology 31-45
   The Creation 32
   Asgard 33
   A Somber View of Life 34-35
   A Family Portrait 36
   Thor 37-38
   The Death of Balder (Baldr) 39-41
   The Tale of the Volsungs and the Nibelungs 42-44
   Goddesses' Rights 45
Egyptian Mythology 46-50
   Ra (Re) 47
   The Creation 48
   Osiris 49
   Mummification 50
The Mythology of India 51-52
Chinese Mythology 53-54
Japanese Mythology 55-56
African Mythology 57-58
Myths of the Polynesians 59-60
Mythology of North America 61-63
   Tricksters: The Raven 62-63
Odds 'n' Ends 64

Pre-test 65
Quizzes 66-72
Post-test 73
Crossword Puzzle 74
Answers to Tests, Quizzes and Puzzles 75-76
Glossary 77
Answers and/or Background Information to Activities 82-95
Bibliography 96

Introduction

The study of mythology is important for a variety of reasons. Mythology holds the key to the understanding of the religions and philosophies of the ancient world. It provides the earliest definitive literary record of the ideals, motives and manners of the ancients. Just as importantly, the knowledge of myths, especially those of the Greeks and Romans, enhances the appreciation of the literature and art of the classical and modern periods.

The objective of this book is to introduce students to various mythologies and to give them a better understanding of the ancient cultures from which the mythologies sprang. It is also intended that the increased knowledge will better enable students to understand and appreciate the many allusions to mythology with which they come in contact in their academic and leisure lives.

The self-directed activities emphasize higher-level thinking skills and have been keyed to Bloom's Taxonomy* for your convenience. Although not so marked, other higher-level skills such as fluency, flexibility, originality and risk-taking are also encouraged.

I hope you enjoy your trip back in time to these ancient worlds!

Bloom's Taxonomy

KNOWLEDGE (K): The recall of specifics and universals; bringing to mind the appropriate material.

COMPREHENSION (C): Understanding what is being communicated and making use of what is being communicated without necessarily relating it to other material or seeing its fullest implications.

APPLICATION (AP): The use of abstractions in particular and concrete situations. The abstractions may be in the form of general or technical ideas, rules or methods which must be remembered and applied.

ANALYSIS (AN): Breaking down a communication into its constituent elements or parts so that the relative hierarchy of ideas expressed are made explicit.

SYNTHESIS (S): Putting together elements and parts to form a whole; arranging and combining the elements in a pattern or structure not clearly there before.

EVALUATION (E): Making judgments about the extent to which material and methods satisfy criteria, either given to the student or determined by the student.

Benjamin Bloom. *Taxonomy of Educational Objectives. Handbook 1: Cognitive Domain.* New York: David McKay, 1956.

What Is Mythology?

*my•thol•o•gy (mĭ-thŏl′-ə-jē)n. pl. -gies. 1.a.** A collection of myths about the origin and history of a people and their deities, ancestors, and heroes. **b.** A body of myths concerning some individual, event, or institution: *"A new mythology, essential to the. . .American funeral rite, has grown up"* (Jessica Mitford). **2.** The field of scholarship dealing with the systematic collection and study of myths. [Fr. *mythologie* ❬ LLat. *mythologia* ❬ Gk. *muthologia*, storytelling: *muthos*, story + *logos*, speech.]

Myths are primitive accounts of the origin, character and functions of the ancient gods, of the origin of humankind, and of the condition of the visible world. The time in which these events occurred is completely different from our time frame.

In primitive cultures it was only natural for the people to have a sense of awe in the presence of the wonders of nature. They attributed to those natural wonders—the sun, the sky, the sea, the mountains, and so on—a free will and personality such as they themselves had. Because they considered themselves inferior to those wonders, however, they believed them to have an even greater freedom, personality and power than they.

Earliest myths were based upon those phenomena that struck the emotions: the feeling of alarm at the crash of thunder; the feeling of gladness in the warm light of day; the feeling of terror in the darkness of night; and the feeling of dread when confronted with death. The first phenomena to strike the mind were probably the changes in night and day, the seasons and the weather. The earliest deities, therefore, were those who presided over the celestial sphere. As time went on, however, every phase of nature and human life was believed to have a controlling deity.

1. Myths present extraordinary events without trying to justify them; therefore, people sometimes confuse them with fables. Analyze the difference between a myth and a fable. (K, C, AN)

_____

_____

_____

_____

_____

_____

*From *The American Heritage Dictionary, Second College Edition.* Boston: Houghton Mifflin Company, 1982.

5

2. The gods and goddesses were identified with the elements of nature over which they presided; therefore, incidents involving the elements of nature—storms, earthquakes, calm weather, and so on—were believed to result from the activities of the gods. Create an original myth to explain a natural disaster such as the San Francisco earthquake of 1906, the eruption of Mt. St. Helens in 1980 or the great Mississippi River flood of 1993. (S)

3. Make a chart entitled ''Characteristics of a Myth.'' Be sure to include such factors as tone, time, plot and main characters. (K, C, AP)

4. Some myths are explanatory in the sense that they explain natural, social, cultural or biological facts. For example, there is a Native American (Abnaki) myth to explain the origin of corn. Research that or another explanatory myth. Summarize the myth and draw a picture to illustrate it. (C, AP)

5. Some philosophers have argued that there is a mythological dimension in all science. They say that myth is what the scientists take for granted as true when they begin to analyze a situation. Take a point of view and write your closing remarks for a debate. (AN, EV, S)

6. Without a knowledge of mythology much of the great literature of the English language could not be fully appreciated. Create a booklet that cites examples of how English poets and prose writers have alluded to (made an indirect reference to) characters and incidents of mythology. (C, AP)

7. Write an original poem that alludes to one or more mythological figures. (C, S)

Preservation of Myths

8. Before the introduction of writing, myths were preserved in the oral traditions by wandering minstrels and bards. Most of what we know today about the mythology of ancient cultures comes from a few important written sources. List at least five of those sources. Make a mobile, bulletin board display or poster. (K, C, AP)

Mythology of the Ancient Greeks

The ancient Greeks, like other primitive peoples, believed that their lives were subject to external powers beyond their control—for example, the weather. Those powers were the "gods" and "goddesses." The gods weren't looked upon as having created the world, but as maintaining and preserving the existing order. They had extraordinary physical strength and were believed to be immortal.

In time the polytheism of the ancient Greeks spread to cover every phase of nature and of human life. The sky, the sea and the earth—everything—had a special guardian and controlling deity. Some of the minor deities were only worshipped in certain areas. For example, there were marine deities that were worshipped only among people connected with the sea. All, however, believed in the superior deities thought to inhabit Mt. Olympus.

Sources of Greek Mythology

One of our most important sources of knowledge about Greek mythology is Homer. Homer is credited with having written the *Iliad* and the *Odyssey;* however, some scholars have doubted that these epics were the work of any one mind.

1. Research the reasons for and against the opinions that Homer wrote the entire poems. Write a paragraph explaining both points of view. Give your opinion as to which is correct. (C, AN, E)

_____

_____

_____

_____

_____

7

2. Find out and list the seven cities that claimed to be the birthplace of Homer. Draw a map of ancient Greece and indicate the locations of those cities. (K, AP)

_____

_____

_____

_____

3. Make a poster or collage that shows how Greek myths have been preserved. (K, C, AP)

4. Simonides was a sixth- to fifth-century B.C. poet. The most important of the fragments which remain of his poetry is the ''Lamentation of Danai.'' It is based upon the tradition that Danai and her infant son Perseus were confined in a chest and set adrift on the sea by order of her father King Acrisius. Acrisius had been warned by the oracle at Delphi that his daughter would give birth to a son who would kill him. Research the story of Perseus. Explain how the oracle's prophecy was fulfilled. (C)

_____

_____

_____

_____

_____

_____

_____

6. The lesser deities, having no place on Olympus, were restricted to localities on Earth where they exercised their powers. Draw three pictures that show where the Naiades, the Oreades and the Dryades lived. Label each. (K, AP)

7. Make a three-generation family tree that shows the ancestry of Zeus two generations back. (K, C, AP)

The Origin of the World:
A Greek Conception

Myths of cosmogony, or the creation of the world, were found in the literature of most peoples.

Many of the ancient Greeks believed that in the beginning there was only Chaos—a confused, shapeless mass. In that mass, however, existed the seeds of things. Earth, sea and air were all mixed together. Then the mass separated into Heaven and Earth. The ocean and the land separated. The Earth, being heavier, sank. The water buoyed up the Earth.

4. Draw the Greek conception of the creation of the universe. (K, AP)

Zeus and the Gods of Mt. Olympus

1. Several of the gods and goddesses have come to Zeus. They have asked him to clarify their areas of responsibility. Complete this chart for Zeus. (K, C)

God or Goddess	Area of Responsibility
Zeus	_____
Hera	_____
Hades	_____
Poseidon	_____
Demeter	_____
Apollo	_____
Artemis	_____
Hephaestus	_____
Athene	_____
Ares	_____
Aphrodite	_____
Hermes	_____
Hestia	_____

2. A new deity has appeared in the Greek pantheon. Prepare an interview between the deity and Zeus. The god or goddess is trying to convince Zeus that he or she should be allowed to dwell in Olympus. (S, E)

Zeus: _____

New Deity: _____

Zeus: _____

New Deity: _____

Zeus: _____

New Deity: _____

Zeus: _____

11

Zeus's Brothers

Poseidon

When Zeus took over the throne from Cronus, besides gaining a general supremacy, he also acquired control of the heavens. To his brother Poseidon fell control of the elements of water. His character and actions were reflected in the phenomena of that element, whether as the great navigable sea, the cloud that allows the grain and vine to grow or as the fountain that refreshes humans, cattle and horses.

1. Though Poseidon was worshipped throughout Greece, he was worshipped in some areas more zealously than in others. Explain why. (C, AN)

_____

_____

2. Athene and Poseidon vied for authority of the region known as Attica. The gods agreed that whoever performed the greatest wonder and at the same time conferred the greatest gift on the land should be entitled to rule over it. Tell what each gave and evaluate the gods' decision to give Attica to Athene. (K, C, AN, E)

_____

_____

_____

Hades

Zeus's brother Hades was given control of the region below the surface of the earth. With the help of Zeus, Hades forcibly seized Persephone, daughter of Demeter and Zeus, from the upper world and took her into his underground kingdom to become his wife. When Demeter could not find Persephone, she wandered all over the world in search of her. On the tenth day she met Helios, the sun, who had witnessed what had happened. He told Demeter of her daughter's fate. Demeter grieved for an entire year, causing it to be the worst year humankind had ever known. At last Zeus realized that he had made a mistake; he sent Hermes to bring back Persephone, provided she hadn't eaten anything. Persephone had already eaten part of a pomegranate, however. It was therefore arranged that she would spend eight months with her mother in Olympus and four months with Hades.

3. Analyze the fact that the Greeks viewed Hades in two opposite ways: as a true friend of mankind and as a grim, relentless deity. (C, AN)

_____

_____

_____

12

4. Some modern versions of the myth say that Persephone remained with Hades during the winter months, but the ancient Greeks believed that she remained in Hades during the hot summer months. Explain the Greek point of view. (C)

_____

_____

_____

_____

The Artist God

From being originally the god of fire, Hephaestus naturally developed into the god of those industries dependent upon fire, such as pottery and metallurgy. (C, AP)

1. Draw a picture of Hephaestus at work. Show one or more of the famous works made by Hephaestus for the gods, goddesses, heroes and heroines of Greek mythology. (C, AP)

2. Hephaestus was the divine personification of the fire that has no connection with the sun or lightning of heaven. Draw a picture that shows how that fire presents itself on earth. (K, C, AP)

The Foolhardy Request:
Phaethon's Downfall

Phaethon was the son of the sea nymph Clymene and Helios, god of the sun; however, he had never met his heavenly father and he felt left out when his friends spoke of their fathers' great accomplishments. One day a schoolmate laughed at Phaethon's boast of being the son of an immortal. Phaethon decided to prove once and for all that he was as he had claimed. Following his mother's advice, he left for the land where the sun rises to ask Helios to acknowledge him as his son.

Phaethon went to the palace of the sun and found Helios awaiting his arrival. Helios was seated on his throne, which glittered with diamonds. Phaethon stopped at a distance, for the light was almost more than he could bear. When Helios asked the purpose of his visit, Phaethon mustered up the courage to tell him; he begged Helios to give him some proof that he was his father.

Helios had no desire to disown his son and confirmed that what his mother had told him was indeed true. As proof, he promised to grant any request that Phaethon might have; however, Helios soon came to regret that promise. Phaethon asked for the chance to drive his father's sun-chariot across the sky. He wanted to make the sun rise and set for just one day.

Helios was dismayed. He never dreamed that his son would make such a foolhardy request. Why, not even the other gods would dare to risk such a journey—not even the great Zeus himself! The god begged his son to change his mind, but it was to no avail. Phaethon insisted upon holding his father to his promise.

Seeing that Phaethon would not change his mind, Helios bathed his son in an unguent to help him endure the scorching flames. He advised him to hold the reins tightly and to keep within the middle zone. He also told Phaethon to go neither too high nor too low, for it was important that all regions get the right amount of heat.

Phaethon took the reins and set out on his fatal journey. It didn't take long for him to wish he hadn't been so stubborn. The winged horses, with no one able to guide them, went wherever their impulses took them. Their high paths caused the heavenly dwellings to burn; their low ones set the Earth on fire! Phaethon felt the heat untolerable.

Finally, Earth begged Zeus for his help. Zeus hurled a mighty thunderbolt against the young charioteer. Phaethon, with his hair on fire, fell like a shooting star into the River Eridanus.

1. Write a possible ending to this myth that would explain an eclipse of the sun. (AP, S)

2. Phaethon felt pressured to prove to his friends that he was the son of a god. Pretend that you are Phaethon's counselor. What advice might you give him regarding peer pressure? (E)

Counselor: _____

_____

_____

3. Peer pressure can be a dangerous thing. Give an example of a time when you felt pressured by your peers to do something you felt was wrong or dangerous. What did you do? If you had it to do over, would you react differently? (AN, E)

_____

_____

_____

_____

4. The sun-god would not break the promise he had made to his son in spite of the fact that he knew it would probably kill him and harm the Heavens and Earth. Judge this decision. Create a cartoon based upon a situation in which you feel a promise should be broken. (AP, S, E)

5. Phaethon did not follow the advice of his father. Another mythological figure who did not heed his father's advice was Icarus. Draw a picture that illustrates the fate of Icarus. (C, AP)

6. Sometimes one must learn by personal experience; other times, that is not feasible. List at least ten things that are too dangerous to learn through personal experience. Describe the ways in which we learn those things. (K, C)

_____

_____

_____

15

Interpreting the Will of the Gods

The ancient Greeks interpreted the will of the gods in a number of ways. One custom, especially in cases of sudden emergency, was the use of augury, or interpretation of signs. For example, sometimes the augury was based on the direction in which a bird was observed to fly overhead. If the bird flew to the right of the augur as he faced north, good luck would follow; if it flew to the left of the augur, bad luck would follow.

Another custom was the consulting of oracles. Apollo, as a symbol of the light of the sun in the sense of an all-seeing and all-knowing power, was regarded as the great god of oracles. Delphi was the main center of his activity. The oracle prophesied by uttering words and sounds while in a state of frenzy. Persons educated in deciphering her prophecies put the sounds into verse. Usually, however, they stated the prophesies in such a cunning way that there was a double meaning. In that way, if a prophecy did not come true, the oracle and her priests could blame it on the way it was interpreted. For example, when the Athenians asked the Oracle at Delphi how to meet the approach of the Persian force, the answer was "Trust to your citadel of wood." The Athenians began to protect the Acropolis with wooden bulwarks, or defensive walls. Themistocles and some of the others, however, persuaded the rest that the "citadel of wood" referred to the fleet. The result was the great victory of the Athenians at Salamis.

Double Trouble

You are a famous oracle. The President of the United States has asked your advice on a current issue. You want to be sure you can say your prophecy was correct no matter how the President interprets it! (S)

Issue: _____

_____

_____

Prophecy: _____

_____

_____

Meaning No. 1: _____

_____

_____

Meaning No. 2: _____

_____

_____

The Judgment of Paris

The myth regarding the judgment of Paris provides a mythical cause of a historical event: the Trojan War.

Paris's parents were King Priam and Queen Hecuba of Troy. The day before his birth, however, Hecuba had a terrible dream. The prophets told her that it meant she would give birth to a child who would cause Troy to be set on fire and destroyed. The king ordered the baby Paris to be taken upon his birth to Mt. Ida and left to die. But a shepherd found and cared for the child; Paris grew up to be strong and handsome.

Years later Paris returned to Troy. When his family learned who he was, they welcomed him—that is, except for his sister Cassandra. Cassandra had been given the gift of prophecy; unfortunately, however, she had offended Apollo, who had given her the gift. Apollo arranged it so that her prophecies, although true, would never be believed. She warned the Trojans in vain that if Paris were allowed to live, Troy would fall!

One day three goddesses—Hera, Athene and Aphrodite—came to visit Paris. At the request of Zeus, they asked him to judge which of them was the fairest. They explained that they had been at the wedding feast of Peleus and Thetis when the goddess Eris threw a beautiful golden apple in their midst. On the apple was written ''To the Fairest.'' Hera, Athene and Aphrodite each believed the apple to be meant for her!

Each of the three goddesses offered to give Paris a special gift if he would choose in her favor. Hera offered great power and riches; Athene offered wisdom, which he could use to win immortal fame as a hero; and Aphrodite offered him the loveliest woman on Earth. He chose Aphrodite and immediately made enemies of the other two.

As it happened, the most beautiful woman on Earth was Helen, wife of Menelaus, king of Sparta. Following the advice of Aphrodite, Paris sailed to Sparta, where he was warmly greeted by Menelaus. When Menelaus was called away, Paris, aided by Aphrodite, seized the opportunity to carry Helen away. Under Aphrodite's spell, Helen could not resist.

When Paris and Helen arrived in Troy, Cassandra once again tried to warn the Trojans of oncoming doom. Once again, no one believed her prophecy.

Hera sent her messenger Iris to tell Menelaus what had happened. He and his brother Agamemnon sent heralds to the other Greek heroes to summon their aid. After two years of preparation, a great fleet of over 1,000 ships was assembled and filled with soldiers. Agamemnon was in command. The Trojan War had begun!

1. The following lines were written by British poet Christopher Marlowe:"The face that launched a thousand ships, and burnt the topless towers of Ilium." To whom do they refer? Explain. (K, C)

_____

_____

_____

2. Write a paragraph telling which of the goddesses you would have chosen if you had been in Paris's place. (AN, E)

_____

_____

_____

3. Keeping in mind that Eris was the goddess of strife, judge her decision to toss the golden apple. (E)

_____

_____

_____

4. Laocoon, a priest of Apollo, warned the Trojans, "Whatever it is, I fear the Greeks most when they make us gifts." Analyze his warning. (AN)

_____

_____

_____

5. Draw a picture that shows how the Greeks tricked the Trojans into opening the gates of Troy. (C, AP)

6. Eris was the goddess of discord and strife. She threw the apple inscribed "To the Fairest" as revenge for not being invited to the wedding. Tell about a time when you felt left out. Then write at least three different ways in which you might have reacted. Tell which way you chose. Do you think you made the best choice? Why or why not? (C, AN, E)

_____

_____

_____

_____

To Arms!

Create a recruitment poster for the Trojan War. You may take either side! (C, AP, S, E)

Messenger Service

Hermes, the messenger of the gods, and Iris, Hera's messenger, have joined forces. They wish to advertise their messenger service. Prepare an ad to help them get more business. (AP, AN, S, E)

19

Lesser Divinities

I. Demigods and Heroes

It seems that demigods, or heroes, were a class of beings unique to the Greeks. They were partly of divine origin and were godlike in their form, strength and courage.

There are three classes of heroes and demigods found in Greek mythology and epic poetry:

Demigods—associated with the creation of humankind and the earliest incidents of human history and civilization. Example: Prometheus

Early Heroes—distinguished for their extraordinary adventures, labors and expeditions. Examples: Heracles, Theseus and Perseus

More Recent Heroes—performed deeds more like historical traditions; magnified by the poets' imagination. Example: Seven Heroes against Thebes

II. Nymphs

The ancient Greeks (and Romans) imagined that every mountain, valley, plain, bush, tree, stream, fountain and lake were filled with beings of a higher order. These beings were called nymphs and were somewhere between gods and humans. They could communicate with both and were generally loved and respected by both. Although they had many of the same powers as the gods—for example, the power to make themselves visible and invisible—they were not destined to immortality.

Prometheus and the Gift of Fire

Many nonliterate societies have myths about a hero who, although not necessarily responsible for the creation, made the world fit for human life—in other words, a hero who created culture. Prometheus is an example of such a culture hero.

Prometheus and Epimetheus were members of a gigantic race of gods known as Titans. Prometheus, whose name meant ''Forethought,'' and Epimetheus, whose name meant ''Afterthought,'' were brothers. It was their job to protect each animal as it came to life. Epimetheus was to give each animal a special gift; Prometheus was to supervise his work.

Epimetheus gave wings to the birds, swiftness to the gazelle and claws to the tiger. To a very slow animal, not very smart, Epimetheus gave a hard shell to help it hide from the world. Each gift he bestowed was more wonderful than the last.

When it came time to give a gift to man (woman wasn't yet created), Prometheus wanted to give the most special gift of all. He was especially fond of man, for he looked so much like himself. Epimetheus, however, had just given out his last gift; he had given quills to the porcupine. Not wanting to leave man helpless, Prometheus asked the goddess Athene for help. She helped him steal a bit of fire from the torch of Helios, the god of the sun.

Prometheus gave the gift of fire to man. Now he could warm himself by the fire. He could learn to make tools to plant crops. He could build towns near where he grew his crops. Prometheus was pleased. He had succeeded in giving the best gift to man.

But Zeus, the ruler of the gods, was not pleased. He was angry that Prometheus had made man greater than the other animals—that he had given man the power of the gods. As punishment, Zeus ordered that Prometheus be captured and bound in chains to a rock on Mt. Caucacus. There Prometheus would remain as an eagle picked at his liver, which grew back as soon as it was devoured. As Prometheus was immortal, he would not die. Instead, he would live in constant pain.

After a while, Zeus offered to free Prometheus if he would tell him a secret he knew, for Prometheus was a prophet. Prometheus would not tell Zeus the secret, but he did tell him one thing; he told him that it would be a man not yet born who would one day save Zeus and the other gods of Mt. Olympus. Although he refused to tell Zeus, Prometheus knew who that man would be. What Prometheus did not know, as he could not foresee his own future, was that the same man would one day set him free.

21

1. Make a poster showing the importance of Prometheus's gift to humankind. (C, AP)

2. Find out who was destined to release Prometheus from his chains and to save the gods of Mt. Olympus from the giants, who would attempt to destroy them. Draw a picture that shows what Prometheus advised his rescuer to do upon leaving him. (C, AP)

3. You are Prometheus's lawyer. Write a letter to Zeus asking him to reconsider his punishment of Prometheus. (AN, S, E)

Zeus
Mount Olympus

Dear Zeus:

_____

_____

_____

_____

_____

_____

_____

_____

Sincerely,

_____

22

Pandora

According to some versions of the myth, Zeus created Pandora, the first woman, in order to punish man for his acceptance of Prometheus's gift of fire. Every god and goddess had contributed something to make her perfect. Aphrodite had given her beauty; Apollo had given her music; and so on. She was given to Epimetheus to become his wife. Prometheus warned his brother to beware of Zeus and his gifts, but Epimetheus would not listen.

Epimetheus had a box in his home containing envy, revenge and all the other evils of the world. He warned Pandora not to open the box. One day, however, Pandora's curiosity got the better of her. She opened up the box; the evils filled the room and rushed out the windows. She tried to replace the lid, but all had escaped—that is, all but hope. And so no matter how bad things are, hope is always with us.

NOTE: In some versions Pandora was sent in good faith with a box containing a blessing from each god. When whe opened the box, all the blessings escaped except for hope.

4. Draw a picture of the evils (or blessings) being set loose. (AP, S)

5. Compare and contrast Prometheus and Epimetheus. (AN)

_____

_____

_____

_____

_____

_____

_____

23

The Twelve Labours of Heracles

Heracles belongs in the group of early heroes distinguished for their extraordinary adventures and services in the cause of human civilization.

Heracles was the son of Zeus and a mortal woman named Alcmene. When Hera found out about him, she sent two serpents to kill Heracles and his twin brother Iphicles (who was not Zeus's son). But the eight-month-old Heracles grabbed one serpent in each hand and strangled them.

As Heracles grew older, he became famous throughout the world for his strength. Hera, however, still wanted to get rid of Heracles and she caused him to have a fit of insanity in which he killed his family. Distraught at what he had done, Heracles went to the Delphic Oracle. The Oracle told him that he must perform ten labours (labors), or tasks, which King Eurystheus would set up. If he succeeded, he would win the right to immortality.

Hera went to the king and told him to give Heracles ten tasks that no mortal could do and to make him do the tasks within twelve years. She also told him to be sure that Heracles died doing them. King Eurystheus agreed.

Nevertheless, Heracles complete the ten tasks and went back to Eurystheus to claim his freedom. The king was furious that Heracles had not died. Claiming that two of the tasks did not count, he added two more.

When Heracles completed those tasks as well, he won his freedom and his right to immortality.

1. List the twelve labours of Heracles. (K)

_____   _____

_____   _____

_____   _____

_____   _____

_____   _____

_____   _____

2. Make a flipbook illustrating each of the twelve labours. (C, AP)

3. Choose a modern Olympic hero or heroine. Write a poem in his or her honor using references to one or more Greek mythological heroes or heroines. (C, AN, S)

4. Invent two additional tasks for Heracles. Write a myth describing his attempts to complete them. (S)

24

Echo and Narcissus

Echo was a beautiful mountain nymph. She had but one fault: she loved to talk and always wanted to have the last word. One day the great Zeus came to her to ask a favor. His wife Hera was very jealous and would not let him out of her sight. He asked Echo to detain Hera so that he could get away from her for a while.

Echo managed to keep Hera busy with her idle chatter, but when Hera learned of the conspiracy against her, she was furious. She said to Echo, "As you have tricked me with your words, from now on you will only be able to repeat what others say to you."

Echo sadly wandered about the forest. Soon it happened that she saw the beautiful youth Narcissus. She immediately fell in love with him and followed him around.

When Narcissus finally heard the noise of her footsteps, he called out, "Is anyone here?"

All poor Echo could answer was, "Here."

When he called out, "Let us meet," she repeated his words and ran to him with outstretched arms.

But Narcissus loved no one but himself and he ran away from her shouting, "I would rather die than you should have me."

From that time on Echo lived in grief in caves and among mountain cliffs. At last all her flesh shrank away and her bones turned into rocks. All that was left of her was her voice, which, as Hera had ordered, continued to have only the last word.

But Narcissus's actions would not go unrevenged. One day one of the many maidens who loved Narcissus in vain uttered a prayer. She prayed that he might know what it was like to love with no return of affection. Nemesis, the goddess of vengeance, granted her wish; she caused Narcissus to fall in love with his own image in the water. Narcissus tried time and time again to kiss or touch the image, but each time it fled. There he remained to gaze upon the image until at last he pined away and died. The gods changed him into a beautiful flower which bears his name.

1. Pretend that you are a narcissist. Write a brief autobiography from that point of view. (C, AP, AN, S)

25

2. Do you think Nemesis's punishment of Narcissus was fair? (E)

_____

_____

_____

_____

3. Give the English meanings of the words *echo, narcissism* and *nemesis.* (C)

Echo: _____

_____

Narcissism: _____

_____

Nemesis: _____

_____

4. The opposite of a narcissist is an altruist. An altruist is someone whose main concern is for others. With altruist at the top of the scale and narcissist at the bottom, how would you rate yourself? Your family? Your friends? Your pet? (E)

Altruist 10	Me _____
9	Mom _____
8	
7	Dad _____
6	
5	Brother(s) _____
4	
3	Sister(s) _____
2	Best Friend _____
Narcissist 1	
	Pet _____

Were you objective and unbiased in your judgment?

_____

_____

_____

_____

Roman Mythology

The ancient Romans in their earliest periods of their history were a pastoral and agricultural people. As they were more united than the Greeks, they had no need for the multitude of deities which the diverse and scattered Greeks found necessary.

When the Romans captured Greece, they adapted many of the Greek ways. Greek literature, philosophy and art became the main basis of education. Many even began to use the Greek language instead of their own. Roman poets often imitated the Greek poets, replacing the names of the Greek deities with Roman gods and goddesses of similar character. In other cases, they changed the form of the Greek name into a Latin one. No real adoption or uniting of the religions took place, however. The Roman ceremonies and forms of worship remained distinct from the Greek.

Because modern scholars became more familiar with the Romans, our ideas about Greek mythology are based in a large part upon the statements made by Roman poets rather than upon those of the Greeks.

Roman Deities

1. Give the accredited Roman equivalent for each of the following Greek deities. (K)

Zeus: Hestia:

Hera: Hephaestus:

Apollo: Ares:

Artemis: Hermes:

Athene: Poseidon:

Aphrodite: Dionysus:

Demeter: Hades:

2. Analyze this statement made by the Roman poet Horace (65 - 8 B.C.): "Captive Greece took her rude conqueror captive." (AN)

_____

_____

_____

_____

Protectors of the Household

The early Romans—before they accepted the ideas about religion and mythology taught to them by the Greeks from southern Italy—worshipped vague and impersonal forces called numina. A numen is a spirit believed to inhabit certain natural phenomena or objects. The numina invoked in family worship were those that guarded their homes and farms.

Vesta

Vesta, known as Hestia by the Greeks, was the goddess of the hearth, or fireside; therefore, she was the guardian of family life. Her priestesses, called vestal virgins, had the responsibility of feeding the sacred flame of her temple, presenting sacrifices and praying for the welfare of the state. They were chosen when they were young girls of six to ten years of age and served in the temple for thirty years.

1. If a vestal virgin let the flame go out, she was severely punished. Draw a diagram to show how the fire would be rekindled. (C, AP)

Janus

2. The Romans tended to ponder the prospects of an undertaking before entering upon it. Use this fact to explain the great honor they paid to Janus. (C, AP)

_____

_____

_____

The Penates and the Lares

3. Draw a picture that shows what the Penates would guard in your home. (C, AP)

4. Write an original story in which your Lares are important characters. (C, S)

Minerva

In Rome the worship of Minerva was carried on as zealously as that of her Greek counterpart, Athene, in Athens. Not only was she the goddess of wisdom, but also the protectress of their arts, industries and domestic skills, such as spinning and weaving.

1. In Rome the object connected with Minerva which was held in highest esteem was the Palladium. Sketch the Palladium and explain its significance to these ancient people. (K, C, AP, AN)

2. According to the myth, Arachne, a mortal maiden, challenged Minerva to compare her skill in weaving with her own. Draw a picture that shows Arachne's fate as a result of that challenge. Judge Minerva's decision to punish her as she did. (K, AP, E)

3. Imagine that you have been turned into an animal of some kind. Write a story that tells how you feel. (S, E)

4. Minerva was a warlike goddess, but she was very unlike Mars, the god of war. Compare and contrast these two deities. (AN)

Cupid and Psyche

Psyche was widely admired for her great beauty. Although Psyche was a modest girl and did not ask to be worshipped, Venus, the goddess of beauty, became very angry. She ordered her son Cupid to use his arrows to cause Psyche to fall in love with a monster. Instead, he fell in love with her himself.

With the help of Apollo's oracle at Delphi, Cupid arranged for Psyche to be brought to a beautiful, but remote palace to become his wife. Everyone believed the groom to be a vile monster. Cupid made himself invisible, but as his words were so filled with love, Psyche was happy. All he asked was that she never try to look at him.

Although Psyche loved her husband, she was very lonely. She convinced Cupid to let her two sisters visit. As they were very jealous of Psyche, they reminded her that her husband might really be a terrible monster waiting to devour her. That, along with her curiosity, convinced her to seek him out with a lamp and a knife—in case their suspicions were correct!

When Psyche saw her beautiful god-husband, she was filled with remorse. Unfortunately, a drop of hot oil fell onto Cupid's shoulder and awakened him. He flew away after telling her that "love cannot dwell with suspicion."

Psyche wandered day and night in search of her husband. At last Ceres advised her to beg Venus for forgiveness. Venus angrily received her and gave her a number of seemingly impossible tasks; after much suffering and torment, Psyche accomplished them all. Then Venus sent her to Proserpina (Persephone in the Greek mythology) in Hades to fetch some of her beauty in a box; she warned Psyche not to look in the box. Again Psyche's curiosity won out, and she opened the box. Out of the box there came a deep sleep which overpowered her.

By now, however, Cupid could no longer bear to be without his beloved Psyche. He found her and brought her back to life. Cupid then begged Jupiter to help. Jupiter granted her immortality and helped the pair win the consent of Venus. Their marriage was celebrated with much rejoicing.

1. The word *psyche* originally meant "soul" but also came to mean "butterfly." Write a poem in which you compare a person's soul to a butterfly. (AN, S)

2. Cupid left Psyche, saying that love cannot dwell with suspicion. What might Psyche have answered in return? (AN, E)

_____

_____

_____

_____

Norse and Germanic Mythology

Germanic mythology refers to the mythology of those peoples who spoke one of the Germanic dialects before they were converted to Christianity. Germanic religion was important in the shaping of European civilization; however, little is known about the gods they worshipped, for most of the ancient Germanic people of the continent and of England were not very literate. Most of what we do know about Germanic religion and mythology comes from literary sources written in Scandinavia—nearly all in manuscripts written in the Old Norse language in Iceland from the twelfth to fourteenth centuries or in later copies of manuscripts written at that time.

1. Analyze the fact that most of the permanent record of the Teutonic, or Germanic, mythology has come from Iceland. (AN)

_____

_____

_____

_____

2. Make a map that shows the modern names of the lands inhabited by the Norsemen. What does the word *Norse* mean? (K, AP)

The greatest sources of Norse mythology are the two collections of verse known as the *Eddas.* The *Elder Edda,* or *Poetic Edda,* was written down in Iceland about A.D. 1270, but contained material much older than that. The *Prose Edda,* or *Younger Edda,* was written down by Snorri Sturluson about A.D. 1220. Actually, the term ''Edda'' began with this book and was later applied to the *Elder Edda.*

The Creation

The story of the beginning of the world is told in three poems of the *Elder Edda*, each giving a different account. In the *Prose Edda* Snorri Sturluson combined the three accounts and added some details from other sources unknown to us.

The Prose Edda Version

In the beginning there was neither sand, sea, nor grass, but only a mighty void called Ginnungagap. On its north side lay the misty, snowy, icy region called Niflheim. To the south was the hot, sunny region of Muspelheim. Eventually, the warm breaths from Muspelheim caused the ice in Niflheim to melt and fall into the Ginnungagap. It was from this matter that the giant Ymir, ancestor of the Frost Giants, sprang. He fed on the four rivers of milk which flowed from the cow Audhumbla, who had been formed from drops of melting ice. Audhumbla herself was nourished by licking salty frost- and ice-covered stones. In fact, she licked the stones into the form of a man, Bori (Buri), who was to become father of Odin and his brothers. Ymir and the Frost Giants ruled until the sons of Bori (Odin and his brothers Vili and Ve) slaughtered Ymir and succeeded that primitive dynasty.

The flesh of the dead Ymir formed the earth: his bones became the rocks and mountains; his teeth became the cliffs; his skull became the heavens; his blood became the sea; and his brains became the clouds that float in the sky. The heavens, the *Edda* tells us, were supported by four Dwarves, called Austri (east), Westri (west), Nordi (north) and Sudri (south). The stars that were in the sky were sparks from the fire-land of Muspelheim. Around the new land, Odin and the other gods built a fence out of Ymir's eyebrows.

1. This newly-created world, called Midgard, would become the home of the mortals. Draw a map that shows why the new world was so named. (C, AP)

2. The mighty evergreen ash was believed to support the universe. Yggdrasil, as it was called, had sprung from the body of Ymir. Draw a picture that shows to where its three huge roots extended. (C, AP)

32

Asgard

From the middle world, or Midgard, arose Asgard, the home of the gods. Originally, there were two races of gods—the Aesir and the Vanir. After a conflict, however, peace was made and they were collectively known as the Aesir, headed by Odin.

1. List the twelve gods of the Aesir. (K)

Odin

1. _____   7. _____

2. _____   8. _____

3. _____   9. _____

4. _____   10. _____

5. _____   11. _____

6. _____   12. _____

2. Asgard, the home of the gods, was accessible only via the bridge called Bifrost. Draw a picture of Bifrost. (C, AP)

33

A Somber View of Life

The world according to the Norse people was a very somber one. Even Asgard, the home of the gods, was grave and joyless. Although they tried their hardest to postpone their fate, the gods knew that they would one day be destroyed by their enemies. The heroes and heroines, too, knew that they would face disaster. Their only hope was to fight a brave death so that they would be entitled to a seat in Odin's castle, Valhalla. There they would remain until Ragnarök (day of doom), when they would join Odin in his losing battle against a monstrous wolf.

The poets of Norse mythology reflected the attitude that even in death there is victory, for true courage cannot be defeated.

1. It has been said that the Norse gods were heroic, but that the Olympian gods could never be heroic. Analyze that statement. (C, AN, E)

_____

_____

_____

_____

Odin

Odin was the greatest of the Norse gods. Not only was he the god of war, but also of wisdom, poetry, prophecy and magic. It was Odin more than any other god who had the responsibility of putting off the day of doom, called Ragnorök, when heaven and earth would be destroyed. In order to best carry out this responsibility, he sought all the knowledge he could get.

2. Odin went to the Well of Wisdom, located below the ash tree, Yggdrasil. The well was guarded by Mimir the Wise. Finish the picture to show how Odin had to pay for the knowledge. (K, AP)

3. Odin wanted to gather as many heroes in Valhalla as possible so that when Ragnarök finally came, he would be able to face the giants in glory. The Valkyries helped him in this regard. Complete the series of pictures to show who the Valkyries were and how they helped Odin. (C, AP)

4. According to Norse mythology, the armor of the Valkyries shed a strange flickering light over the northern skies. Name this phenomenon and give a scientific explanation for it. (C)

_____

_____

_____

_____

5. Odin's name meant rage or fury. Although he was the god of wisdom, he was also the god of war. He was often immoral and even broke the most sacred of oaths, the oath on the holy ring. Odin's worship seems to have spread during the eighth to tenth centuries. Use this last fact to explain Odin's character. (AP, AN)

_____

_____

_____

_____

A Family Portrait

Loki is one of the most puzzling figures in Norse mythology. Although he was not a god, he was allowed in Asgard as he wished—supposedly because of a bargain he had made with Odin. He often caused trouble for the gods, although he sometimes helped get them out of the trouble he had caused. Loki was viciously cunning and could not be trusted.

1. Loki and Angrboda, or Distress-Bringer, were the parents of three evil children. Draw their pictures as they might appear in a family album.

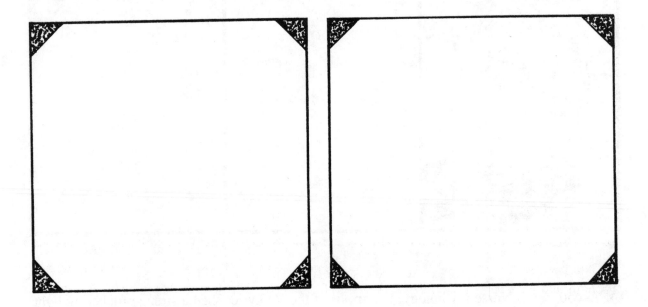

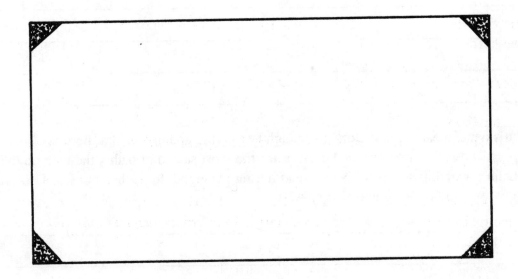

Thor

Thor, the son of Odin, was the strongest of the gods. He was a friend to mankind and enemy of the giants. He seems to have been worshipped in Iceland and throughout the north to a greater extent than any other god. This is evidenced by the great number of place-names in his honor.

1. Thor's home was Bilskirnir. Write an ad for the classified section of the paper to help Thor sell his home. (K, C, AP)

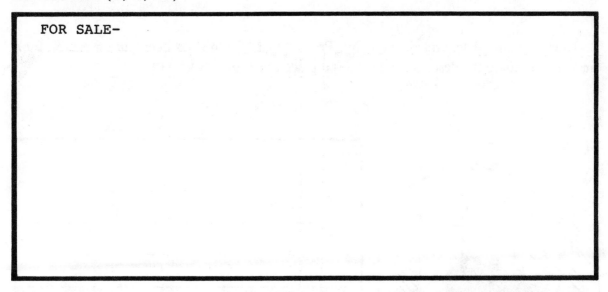

```
FOR SALE-
```

Thor possessed three sacred objects: a hammer called Mjollnir, a belt which doubled his strength and iron gloves which increased the force of his blows with the hammer.

The Theft of Thor's Hammer

Every day Thor did his best to fight the giants and to show the strength of the gods. He slew the nine-headed giant, Trivaldi; he killed Geirrod, the fire-gaint. It was a never-ending battle.

One day Thor realized that his hammer, Mjollnir, had been stolen by Thrym, a frost-giant. Although the gods didn't really trust Loki, they knew that as a giant, Loki would have a better chance than they to get the hammer back. They convinced Loki that he, too, would be in danger if Thrym kept the hammer; therefore, Loki went north to Thrym's realm to find Mjollnir.

When Loki returned, he reported that Thrym had buried the hammer eight fathoms deep under the rocks of Jötunheim. Thrym had agreed to return the hammer only if he could have Freyja, the goddess of love, for his wife.

The goddess Freyja, however, would not give in to such an arrangement. Instead, Thor dressed in Freyja's clothes and went with Loki, who was dressed as a bridesmaid, to Jötunheim.

Thrym was surprised when his bride-to-be ate eight salmon and a huge black ox and gulped down three gallons of mead (a foaming ale which the gods and heroes of Valhalla drank)! He became startled when he saw that his bride's eyeballs glistened with fire. Loki explained Freyja's hunger by saying that she had fasted for eight days because of her great desire to see him. He explained the fire in her eyes in a similar way. Both Loki and Thor were relieved when Thrym accepted Loki's explanations.

Thrym planned to break the bargain he had made and to keep both the hammer and the goddess. When Thrym ordered that the hammer be placed on Freyja's lap, however, Thor pulled off his disguise. He grabbed his precious Mjollnir and with it slew Thrym and his followers.

2. Thor's hammer had a magical quality. Pretend that Mjollnir has been put on exhibit for a museum. Prepare the descriptive card to be placed next to it. (A, AP)

Mjollnir

3. Thor's hammer was smithed by Dwarves, or Black Elves. Research dwarves and elves in Norse mythology. Compare and contrast the two groups of beings: Black Elves and Elves of Light. (C, AN)

_____

_____

_____

_____

The Death of Balder (Baldr)

Balder, the son of Odin and the goddess Frigga, was the most beloved of all the gods. His name meant the shining god, but he was also known as Balder the Good, Balder the Innocent and Balder the Beautiful. Wherever he went, he radiated peace and well-being.

Balder had been tormented with terrible dreams which foreboded his death; however, his dreams gave him no hint as to the means of his death. The gods tried to figure out every possible way Balder might be destroyed so that his death might be prevented, but the possibilities were endless.

Balder's mother, Frigga, decided to visit every thing, both living and non-living. She spoke to fire, water, metals, trees, stones and illnesses. She spoke to every creature that ever walked, crawled, swam or flew. Each of these took an oath that they would not harm her son.

On her way home, however, Frigga realized that she had overlooked the mistletoe. Thinking it too young and puny to do Balder any harm, she continued on her way. She and the other gods felt secure that nothing on heaven or earth could do Balder harm.

Although Odin knew that Balder must die, the other gods believed he was now invulnerable and they made up a game. In order to honor him they threw axes, clubs and any other weapons they could think of at him. Each bounced gracefully off his shining body.

One day, however, the evil Loki, who seemed to enjoy bringing the gods into difficulty, found out about the mistletoe. He cut a sprig of mistletoe and whittled the stem until it had a very sharp point. Loki took the mistletoe to Asgard and there he saw the gods hurling their weapons at Balder. He noticed that Balder's blind brother, Hoder, was standing by himself.

Loki changed his voice and convinced Hoder to take part in the games. Telling Hoder that he would guide his hand, Loki aimed the deadly mistletoe at Balder. Balder fell to the ground.

Each god tried to bring Balder back to life, but to no avail. They even sent Hermod, the swiftest of the gods, to see Hel, the goddess of the dead, to beg for Balder's release. Hel agreed to the release provided that **all** things of the world, both living and dead, wept for him. All things willingly complied except for an old giantess, again believed to be Loki in disguise.

And so Balder was prevented from returning to Asgard. He was to remain in Niflheim, land of the dead, until that final battle and the world's end.

1. Loki was finally punished for his treatment of Balder. Find out how the gods punished him. Write an account of an earthquake for a local newspaper based upon the punishment. (K, C, AP, S)

Asgard

_____   _____

_____   _____

_____   _____

_____   _____

_____   _____

_____   _____

_____   _____

2. Write an acrostic poem about Balder. (S, E)

Balder

B _____

A _____

L _____

D _____

E _____

R _____

3. Hermod used Odin's horse Sleipner to ride to the goddess Hel. Describe Sleipner. (K, C)

_____

_____

_____

_____

4. Balder represented the sun. The joy of the world in the presence of Balder represented the gladness inspired by the sunlight. Write a poem about the season in which you allude to Balder. (S)

40

5. In later times, storytellers changed the ending to make it a happier one. In the more modern versions Frigga was able to bring Balder back to life. The tears which she had shed for her son were transformed into the pearly white berries of the mistletoe plant. From that point on; the mistletoe would never harm anyone. Draw a picture of a custom regarding the mistletoe that came about because of this modern version of the myth. (C, AP)

6. Frigga and the other gods thought the mistletoe was too lowly to worry about. Find out how the mistletoe grows. Use that information to explain Frigga's attitude towards the mistletoe. (C, AP)

_____

_____

_____

_____

7. Do you think that anyone besides Loki should be held responsible for Balder's death? (Hoder? Frigga? the other gods and goddesses? Balder himself?) Give your opinion. (E)

_____

_____

_____

_____

_____

The Tale of the Volsungs and the Nibelungs

The *Volsunga Saga* (a thirteenth-century Icelandic prose narrative) and the *Nibelungenlied* (a Middle-High-German narrative poem, written c. 1200) are very similar in content. They tell the tale of the Volsungs and the Nibelungs, heroes of myths and legends dating back to the Teutonic (Germanic) migrations.

The most popular of these epic poems was that of Sigurd (Siegfried in German) the Volsung, the favorite hero of Norse mythology. He was also the subject of many poems in the *Elder Edda*.

Sigurd and Brynhild

Sigurd was the greatest of all the Volsungs. He had been taught well in all the arts and sciences by his foster father, Regin. But Regin was very greedy and used Sigurd to try to get back a hoard of gold which Regin claimed as his. He incited Sigurd to slay Fafnir, the dragon who guarded the treasure. Sigurd slew the dragon and ate of its heart, thereby learning the language of the birds. The birds advised Sigurd to kill Regin, for he was plotting against him. Although it saddened him, he followed their advice.

Sigurd took the treasure, which included a magic ring, and mounted his horse Greybell. What he did not know was that both the gold and the ring had been cursed by Andvari the dwarf, their previous owner. Eventually, Sigurd arrived at the Hill of Hindfell. There he saw a circle of fire, in the middle of which slept the lovely maiden Brynhild (Brunhilde, in German). Brynhild was the most beautiful of all the Valkyries. She had disobeyed Odin and Odin decided to punish her by putting her into a deep sleep until a mortal man awakened her. Before being put to sleep, however, Brynhild begged that only a man whose heart knew no fear be allowed to wake her. Odin fulfilled her request and surrounded her couch with a flaming fire through which only the bravest would venture.

Sigurd rode through the flames and awakened the beautiful Brynhild. He then gave her the ring he had taken from the dragon, still not knowing it was cursed. Although Sigurd loved Brynhild and she loved him, Brynhild, who could foresee the future, knew their love was doomed.

It happened that after leaving Brynhild, Sigurd went to the court of the Nibelungs. He was treated well by King Giuki and his three sons, Gunnar (Gunther), Hogni and Guttorm. But the king also had a daughter—Gudrun (Kriemhild)—who loved Sigurd and wanted to marry him; therefore, Gudrun's mother, Grimhild, used a magic potion to make Sigurd forget Brynhild. The potion worked, and soon Sigurd and Gudrun were married, leaving Brynhild to await another hero to rescue her from the fire.

Gunnar, Gudrun's brother, wanted to marry Brynhild, but he was not brave enough to ride through the flames. Sigurd came to his aid. He disguised himself as Gunnar and again rode through the flames of Hindfell. Still pretending to be Gunnar, he asked Brynhild to come to the land of the Nibelungs to become his wife. She consented and the two exchanged rings, she returning to him the cursed ring of Andvari.

Brynhild was aware of the deceit that had been played on her, but she said nothing. She would marry Gunnar as she had agreed. At the wedding, however, Grimhild's potion wore off. When Sigurd looked upon the lovely Brynhild, he once again felt the same feelings of love. Still, Brynhild went on as if nothing were wrong. It wasn't until Gudrun insulted Brynhild by gloating over the details of the deceit and throwing the ring in her face that Brynhild resolved to have her revenge.

Brynhild arranged it so that Guttorm, Gunnar's brother, would be incited to slay Sigurd. Guttorm stabbed him while he was asleep and thus ended the life of the hero. Brynhild, overcome with grief (for she still loved Sigurd) dealt herself a mortal wound and was burned on the funeral pyre with Sigurd.

1. Richard Wagner composed a series of four operas based upon the stories of the Volsungs and the Nibelungs. What is his tetralogy (series of four) called? (K)

_____

_____

_____

_____

Design a billboard poster advertising the performance of Wagner's tetralogy. (S)

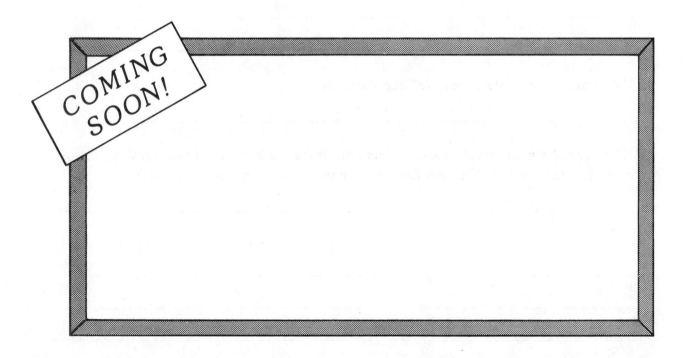

43

2. If you were Brynhild, would you have married Gunnar even though you knew he had deceived you? Why or why not? (AN, E)

_____

_____

_____

_____

3. Judge Brynhild's decision to take revenge upon Gudrun and Sigurd. (E)

_____

_____

_____

_____

Gudrun, while grieving for Sigurd, married Atli, unsurpassed for power and terror. The treacherous Atli invited Gudrun's brothers to Hunland so that he might seize the golden treasure they had gotten from Sigurd. Although the heroes foresaw their unhappy destiny, they went anyway. They faced their fate courageously and did not surrender the hoard, which was buried at the bottom of the Rhine River.

4. Atli represents a historical figure, sometimes called the ''Scourge of the Gods.'' Who was he? (K)

_____

_____

_____

5. What might the ''golden treasure'' represent? (C)

_____

6. The story of Sigurd, Brynhild and Gudrun reflects the somber Norse character and point of view. Analyze the effect of natural conditions upon that point of view. (C, AN)

_____

_____

_____

_____

Goddesses' Rights!

Write a letter to Odin complaining that the goddesses of Asgard are not as important as those of Mt. Olympus. Also write Odin's response. (C, AP, AN)

Dear Odin:

_____

_____

_____

_____

_____

_____

_____

Sincerely,

A Citizen for Goddesses' Rights

Dear Citizen:

_____

_____

_____

_____

_____

_____

_____

Knowingly,

Odin

Egyptian Mythology

In predynastic times (before c. 3100 B.C. when Egypt was united) each settlement had its own god. Like the early deities of most prehistoric cultures, the early Egyptian gods and goddesses were associated with the forces of nature. These gods were originally pictured as animals. For example, Anubis was pictured as a jackal, Horus as a falcon and Buto as a snake.

Anubis   Horus   Buto

As time went on, the gods were given human forms and qualities. Anubis still retained his jackal's head, but now had a man's body. Horus now had the body of a man and the head of a falcon. In many cases, the god no longer looked like the animal at all, but was accompanied by the animal or wore a symbol of it.

Because a god represented his city, his power often fluctuated with the power of the city. In other words, if a city grew in importance, so did its god. If one city was victorious in battle over another city, its god was also believed to have conquered that city's god. The conquered gods did not cease to exist. They continued to have control over local matters; however, they were under the authority of the gods which had conquered them—just as the conquered cities still existed under the rule of their conquerors.

Before the union of Upper and Lower Egypt, Set (Seth) was regarded as the supreme god in Upper Egypt and Horus in the Delta. After the union Horus was regarded as the supreme god of all Egypt. All the other gods accepted the authority of Horus.

1. Details of Egyptian mythology were changed from time to time. Names of the deities often changed. The attributes and powers associated with certain gods were taken away and given to other gods. Analyze the reasons for this. (AN)

_____

_____

_____

_____

Ra (Re)

Ra was different from the other Egyptian deities in that he was never a local god. He originally was the god of the physical attributes of the sun; however, he later became the supreme god of all Egypt. Ra became associated with many other gods who were manifestations of his various attributes: Horus as the strong young sun of the day; Amun of Thebes as the hidden and mysterious power of the sun that sustains the universe; Mentu as the rising sun; Atmu as the setting sun; and Shu as the solar light.

1. A temple was built to Ra at Heliopolis in North Egypt; a large staff of priests resided there. This was long before such institutions were common. Compare and contrast Ra and his Greek counterpart, Helios. (AN)

_____

_____

_____

_____

_____

2. Draw a picture of a scarab. What did it represent? (K, C)

3. One of the gods identified with Ra (Re) was Amun, the chief god of Upper Egypt. Amun (also known as Ammon, Amon, Amen, Amen-Ra and Amun-Num) represented the power that creates and sustains the universe. Amun was the god of Thebes. His identification with the sun-god was largely due to the work of his priests. Why would the priests of Amun want him to be associated with Ra? (C, AN)

_____

_____

_____

47

The Creation

There were various versions of the creation of the world and the arrangement of the gods and goddesses. A popular version was a "triad," or trinity. It presented Geb, the Earth, as Ra's father and Nut, the Sky, as his mother.

The mythographers at Heliopolis, the center of Ra's worship, did their best to spread another view. The version they presented was an "ennead," or ninefold divinity.

1. Draw a genealogical chart representing the ennead. (K, C, AP)

2. During the Fifth Dynasty there was a change which greatly affected the theology of Egypt. Explain. (C, AN)

_____

_____

_____

_____

3. According to Egyptian mythology, Geb and Nut lived together until Shu ordered them to live separately. Draw a picture that shows how the Egyptians pictured Nut, Geb, Shu and Ra. (C, AP)

Osiris

Osiris was the most human and the kindest of the gods. He was murdered by his evil brother Set (Seth). Set, who was the god of darkness, had tricked Osiris into a coffin, which he threw into the Nile. Later he opened the coffin and cut Osiris's body into fourteen pieces, which he scattered throughout Egypt.

1. Draw a series of pictures that shows how Osiris's wife Isis and his son Horus reacted to Osiris's murder. (C, AP)

Osiris became the judge of the underworld. An ostrich feather, the symbol of *maat*, was placed on a scale to be weighed against the dead person's heart. The goddess Maat stood for truth, order and justice. Osiris studied the scale and presented his verdict.

2. Suppose Osiris weighed your heart against the symbol of Maat. What would be his verdict? (E)

3. Osiris's soul was believed to inhabit the body of Apis, the Bull of Memphis. At the death of the bull, Osiris's soul was transferred to his successor. Research the qualifications necessary for a bull to be worshipped as Apis. Draw a picture of Apis on another sheet of paper. (C, AP)

4. Pretend that you are Horus. Prepare a speech to the council made up of the ennead and the other gods. In the speech you accuse Seth of the cruel murder of your father, Osiris, and the usurpation of the throne of Egypt. (C, AP, S)

Mummification

To ancient Egyptians, life after death was even more important than their lives on Earth. It was, therefore, imperative that when a person died—especially a person as important as a pharaoh—the body be preserved and protected.

To preserve the body, a system of embalming and drying, called mummification, was practiced. The heart was left in the body, but the other organs were placed in objects called "canopic jars." The body was washed with wine and spices and covered with salts. It was left for up to seventy days to dry. Then, to protect the body, it was placed in a royal coffin and laid to rest in the tomb.

1. In the case of the pharaohs, ordinary tombs were not enough. Draw a picture to show the magnificent tombs which the pharaohs had built for their afterlives. (C, AP)

2. The Egyptians believed that one's afterlife was similar to one's life on Earth; therefore, they buried with the person all the objects (or models of the objects) which the person might need. List the ten things that you would most want buried with you if you believed in an afterlife similar to your life on Earth. (E)

_____   _____

_____   _____

_____   _____

_____   _____

_____   _____

3. The Sphinx was worshipped as a form of the Sun God called Harmarchis. Use clay to make a model of the Sphinx. (C, AP)

The Mythology of India

The oldest sacred writings of the Hindus are called Vedas. They were written between 2000 and 1000 B.C. The *Regveda,* or *Veda of Verses,* has given us a great deal of knowledge about the gods. Although the gods were somewhat concerned with moral and ethical matters, they were primarily personifications of the forces of nature.

1. Find out the name of the ancient Indic language which is the language of Hinduism and the Vedas and which is the classical literary language of India. (K)

_____

2. List at least six deities of the Vedas. (K)

_____   _____

_____   _____

_____   _____

Agni, the youngest of the gods, was also one of the most important. He was both good and bad, helpful and destructive.

3. Tell how Agni was born. Explain his two-sided nature. (C, AN)

_____

_____

_____

_____

_____

Varuna, with his 1,000 eyes, was all-seeing and all-knowing. It was his job to judge sinners. He carried out this responsibility fairly but with a certain amount of severity.

4. Pretend that you have been given the powers of Varuna. No man, woman or child can keep a secret from you. How does this power make you feel? Would you rather not have it? Explain. (AN, E)

_____

_____

_____

_____

The Brahmanic Deities

The *Upanishads* and *Brahmanas*, written several hundreds of years after the Vedic Age, elaborated on the earlier Vedas. The old gods of the Vedas were transformed from gods who simply personified aspects of nature to those who represented the relationships of human beings to the world in which they lived. From these philosophical works eventually came Hinduism, the contemporary religion of India.

The chief gods of the later Hindu religion formed a triad, or trinity. They are not separate, independent gods, but three manifestations of one supreme being, Brahm.

1. Name the three gods of the Hindu trinity. (K)

_____   _____   _____

2. Make a poster that shows how Brahma, Vishnu and Shiva are usually pictured. Briefly explain the three phases of Brahm's energy. (C, AP)

Vishnu: Guardian of the Universe

According to Hindu mythology, Vishnu guards the universe and protects the world from impending danger. From time to time, Vishnu is born as a man in order to save and teach mankind.

One of the times Vishnu was born a man was when a terrible demon had defeated the gods and taken control of earth, the heavens and the underworld. Vishnu was born in the form of a dwarf to a kindly couple who lived alone in the forest. They raised him until he was old enough to perform his task.

At last the lord of the three worlds declared that as part of a sacrificial ceremony he would give a generous gift to all who asked. Vishnu, still in the form of a dwarf, approached the demon. He asked the demon for as much land as he could cover with three steps. Thinking the amount of land the dwarf could cover to be very small, the demon laughed and agreed.

Then Vishnu revealed his true form. In just three strides he stepped from the underworld to Earth and the Heavens. The world was saved from the terrible demons.

1. Just as it was Vishnu's job to preserve the world, it was Shiva's job to destroy it. Yet Shiva did not destroy out of malice. Explain. (C)

_____

_____

_____

52

Chinese Mythology

Chinese mythology is derived from three great religions: Taoism, Confucianism and Buddhism. Taoism is based upon the teachings of Lao-tse, who lived in the sixth century B.C. Confucianism is based upon the teachings of the Chinese philosopher Confucius; it deals more with ethical matters than with mythology. Buddhism was brought to China from India in 300 B.C. The result of that influence was the formation of a trinity which paralleled that of the Buddhist pantheon. The Taoist trinity consisted of Lao-tse, who became deified after his death, Pan Ku and Yu Huang Shangti.

Chinese myths explain not only the origin of the universe, but also the particular aspects of Chinese civilization and culture. They deal with the actions of gods and other supernatural beings as those actions relate to the everyday lives of men and women. There was a god to cover every aspect of civilization, as well as nature. For example, there were gods to protect the home and the city, as well as gods in charge of lightning, thunder, etc.

Although there were undoubtedly a wealth of myths in ancient China, we have little knowledge of them. Most of what we know about Chinese mythology dated from c. the fifth century B.C. and later.

1. As in many mythologies, creation was seen as the act of reducing chaos to order. Above is a picture of the egg of Chaos. It represents the Great Unity. The two sections are the Yin and the Yang. Analyze the two opposing forces of Yin and Yang. (AN)

_____

_____

_____

_____

_____

_____

Pan-ku was born of the egg of Chaos, which is composed of the symbols of Yin and Yang. He lived for 18,000 years and grew ten feet a day. His body filled the space between Heaven and Earth. When he finally died, the parts of his body became various natural elements. According to some texts, the four cardinal mountains (directions) were derived from his dead body.

2. Make a chart showing the symbolic animals of the four cardinal directions, which grew from the dead Pan-ku. Include the direction, season, color and element each animal represented. (K, AP)

3. Draw a picture of the Phoenix. (C, AP)

4. Find out who Yü the Great was in Chinese mythology. Pretend that Yü is being given a dinner in his honor. Write a testimonial speech honoring Yü. (C, S, E)

5. Draw a picture that shows how dragons and tortoises helped Yü accomplish his greatest task. (C, AP)

The dragon plays an important role in Chinese mythology. Unlike the dragons of other cultures, the Chinese dragon is held in high esteem. For the most part, it bestows blessings on humankind. As the dragon moves through the heavens, he gathers moisture; he gives out that moisture in the form of rain. Of course, just as rain is vital to life and yet at times destructive, the dragon, too, is occasionally destructive.

6. Use watercolors or dyes to paint a picture of a dragon in the Chinese style. (C, AP, S)

Ten Suns

According to Chinese mythology, there were at one time ten suns. They were the offspring of the goddess Hsi Ho and Ti Chün (a manifestation of Shang Ti, or Lord on High). Every morning Hsi Ho bathed the suns in a beautiful pond that restored their brightness. The ten suns took turns shedding light upon the world. The nine who were not on duty rested on a giant fu-sang tree, located on the eastern edge of the world. The tenth sun travelled on his dragon-drawn chariot until reaching the jo tree in the west, where the sun finally set.

7. The fact that there is now only one sun is explained by the myth regarding the saviour-hero Hou I. Create an illustrated booklet for children that tells the story of how the suns threatened the world and how Hou I saved the world from destruction. (C, AP)

Japanese Mythology

Shinto, the religion indigenous to Japan, borrowed a great deal from the mythologies of Taoism, Confucianism and Buddhism. The two main books of the Shinto religion are the *Koji-ki* and the *Nihon-gi*. Both were written in the eighth century A.D. *Koji-ki* deals with the age of the gods before the creation of man. It describes how the islands of Japan were created by the gods and deliberately located in the center of the world. *Nihon-gi* explains how the emperors of Japan all directly descended from the Sun-Goddess.

1. Write a synonym for *indigenious*. (K) _____

2. The worship of the sun is very important in the Shinto religion. The rising sun is even symbolized in the Japanese national flag. There is a difference, however, in the way the sun is presented in the Shinto religion as compared to other religions. Explain. (K, C)

_____

_____

_____

_____

3. Ama-Terasu hid in a cave because of the vicious pranks of her brother Susa-no-o. Draw a picture that shows the result of her action. (C, AP)

4. In what way is the myth of Ama-Terasu similar to that of the Greek Demeter? (C, AP)

_____

_____

_____

55

The Creation

Long ago, before the creation of the world, there were only heaven, earth and ocean. When seven generations of divine beings had come into being, the older gods decided that it was time to create the world. They sent two gods from the youngest generation down from the High Plain of Heaven to accomplish that task. The two gods they sent were Izanagi, a male, and Izanami, a female. The first lands to be created by these divine beings were the beautiful islands of Japan.

5. Use watercolors to paint a picture that shows how Izanami and Izanagi created the world. (C, AP, S)

In the process of creating the world, Izanami gave birth to the god of fire. As a result, she was burned to death and went to the land of darkness, called Yomi. Izanagi came to look for her. When he found her, she told him not to look at her. Izanagi did not follow her instructions. He broke off a tooth of his hair comb and lit it as a torch. Seeing Izanami's decayed body, Izanagi fled. The angry Izanami sent the Ugly Women of Yomi to kill him; however, Izanagi managed to escape.

6. Find out how Izanagi escaped. Write an all-points bulletin to be on the lookout for Izanagi. Describe his escape from the Ugly Women of Yomi. (C, AP)

_____

_____

_____

_____

_____

_____

_____

7. Japanese mythology is rich in stories of supernatural creatures. Compare and contrast the tengu, the oni and the kappa. (AN)

_____

_____

_____

_____

_____

African Mythology

It is difficult to generalize about African mythology because there are so many different peoples living on the continent. Although the myths are varied in detail, however, they do have some things in common. First of all, there seems to be a universal belief in survival and triumph over death.

Study of African mythology is made more difficult by the fact that there are no ancient written collections. Although there was no writing in ancient Africa, however, the people did record their thoughts and feelings through art. The art was used to express every aspect of life and in a way may be considered the ''sacred literature'' of Africa.

God Leaves the World

According to many African myths, God at one time lived either on Earth or, more commonly, in a very low sky. In fact, in most African mythologies God was actually identified with the sky. In most cases humans did something to anger God, causing him to leave Earth and go up to Heaven where he wouldn't be bothered. In several of the myths females are blamed for the misfortune, probably because the stories were told by the men! In some places it is told that the women picked off pieces of the sky to use as an ingredient in their dinners; in other places it is said that the women knocked against the sky with their pestles as they pounded their corn into grain. Some even tell of children wiping their greasy hands against the low sky after eating.

1. Create a comic strip that illustrates one version of the myth accounting for God's living in Heaven. (C, AP)

2. The Supreme Being is pictured as living in Heaven and as being especially concerned with rain. Explain why the Supreme Being is rarely associated with the sun in African mythology. (C, AN)

_____

_____

_____

_____

The Origin of Death

Another universal element in African mythology is the idea that human death is unnatural and did not always exist. It is blamed in most cases on a messenger sent by God to tell humans what to do so that they wouldn't die. The messenger is usually an animal, especially the dog or the chameleon. In some myths the messenger deliberately caused a delay in delivering the message; in others, the delay was unintended.

At one time there were only three humans: a man, a woman and their baby boy. The Supreme Being told them that they would not die. God explained that when they reached old age, they should put on their new skins, which would be delivered to them by Dog.

Dog left with their bundle of skins with all good intentions; however, on the way he met a group of animals feeding on rice and pumpkins. He accepted their invitation to join them. In the course of their conversation, Dog explained the contents of his bundle. Snake stole the bundle and he and the other snakes kept the skins for their own use.

Dog confessed to the humans that he had carelessly allowed the skins to be stolen. Unfortunately, it was too late. From that time on, death would come to mankind. Snake was allowed to keep the skins, but he and the other snakes were punished by being driven away from towns to live a lonely existence.

3. The above myth accounts for not only the origin of death, but also the snake's shedding of its skin. Make a poster that shows the stages in a snake's shedding of its skin and explain what happens in each stage. (C, AP)

4. Because the snake sheds its skin yet continues to live, it is often considered in mythology to be immortal. When shown with its tail in its mouth, it often represents eternity. Draw a picture in the African style of the ''snake of eternity.'' (AP)

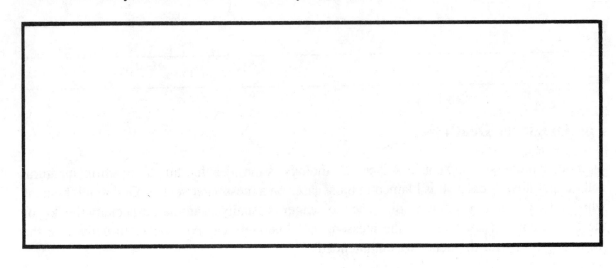

Myths of the Polynesians

The scattered islands of the Central and South Pacific are known as Polynesia, and the native people who inhabit those islands are called Polynesians. There are many similarities among the myths and legends of these different peoples, although—especially among the Hawaiians—there were special local deities as well.

1. Draw a map of Polynesia and label the islands. (K, C, AP)

Creation Myths

As with many primitive peoples, there were several versions of the creation. According to a Tahitian myth, the god Tiki existed from the very beginning when all that appeared was ocean. Tiki floated upon the water in his canoe. Eventually, he dug up the land, which had been hidden under the ocean, thereby creating the world.

Another creation myth tells of the god Taaroa, who lived in the heavens in a huge egg. When he broke out of the egg, he created a daughter. Taaroa and his daughter then made the earth, sea and sky. A similar myth tells of a huge bird dropping a gigantic egg into the primeval sea. When the egg broke itself open, the world was created.

2. According to Hawaiian mythology, the Heavens and Earth were created by Kane, the chief god, with the help of the other principal deities: Ku, Lono and Kanaloa. Research the Hawaiian myth of creation. Explain the Heavens and the Earth. Draw a picture to illustrate it. (C, AP)

Pele

The goddess Pele lived on Floating Island with her brothers and sisters, all of whom were ruled by the eldest brother, Ka Moho, the god of steam. Steam God ordered his brother Fire-Keeper God to teach Pele the secrets of fire-making. Once she learned them, however, she angered her sister Namaka, Sea Goddess, for use of these secrets caused many fish to die. Seeing there would never be peace, Ka Moho ordered Tide and Current to help Pele find a new home. Pele went to Kauai, but Namaka followed and put out her fire by causing a great storm. The same thing happened at Oahu and Maui. Finally, Pele went to the island of Hawaii, where the Great Kilauea was located. The crater had been the home of Forest-Eater. Forest-Eater could not be found, but Pele made the crater her home. Namaka decided that she could never kill her sister and finally decided to ignore her.

59

3. How might the people use this myth to explain the difference between the volcanoes of Hawaii and those of Kauai, Oahu and Maui. (AN)

_____

_____

_____

_____

_____

_____

_____

4. Draw a picture of Great Kilauea after Pele has been angered. (C, AP)

Mythology of North America

The religious ideas of Native Americans varied from tribe to tribe because their lifestyles and needs varied. Basically, however, the gods were personifications of nature. Every aspect of nature was believed to be possessed by spirits; sometimes these spirits were benevolent and sometimes they were malevolent. The sun was the most important god to some tribes, while rain gods were more important to others.

Animals were deified in many tribal mythologies. Tribes that were dependent upon hunting for survival often deified the animals they hunted. For example, they might believe that there was a Super Buffalo or a Super Deer who had the power to cause the hunting season to be a success or a failure.

In other tribes—especially along the Northwest Pacific Coast—animals were deified in a different way. Each clan within those tribes had its own totem animal. That animal was believed to be the supernatural ancestor of the family.

Pueblo Indians of the Southwest

The Pueblo religion was among the most elaborate of all North American tribes. Most Pueblo tribes believed in kachina spirits. Masked dancers performed rituals which were carefully rehearsed. Their deer- or buffalo-hide masks symbolized the kachina's powers. The dancers prayed for such things as sunshine, rain and a good harvest. It was believed that if all the steps and gestures were performed correctly, the kachinas would be present and would respond favorably to their requests.

1. Which were more important to the Pueblos: rain gods or sun gods? Explain. (C)

_____

_____

_____

_____

_____

2. Paint a picture that illustrates the Pueblo Snake Ceremony. (C, AP)

3. Ceremonies were lightened by the presence of Mudheads and Koshare. Design the make-up and costume for a Koshare. (C, AP)

Tricksters: The Raven

Many Native American tribes had stories about a mischievous animal-god, or trickster. Along the Northwest Coast that trickster was Yehl, the Raven. Although Raven is a troublemaker, he often comes to the aid of human beings as well. In many of the tales, Raven is said to have played a part in the creation of the world.

According to one of the myths, there were at one time twin Ravens, both snow white: one was good and one was bad. The good Raven created perfect creatures only to have the bad Raven spoil them by adding an imperfection. One day the good Raven was admiring the beautiful fish he had created. His evil brother saw the perfect creature and stepped on its middle, turning it into a flat flounder. For the first time the good Raven experienced hate. He threatened to kill his evil twin if he didn't stop ruining his creations.

When the evil Raven instead tried to kill the good Raven, the good Raven was prepared. He struck his brother with an axe, the only way either Raven could have been killed. But the good Raven soon felt remorse for what he had done. He tried to wipe away his brother's blood, but he could not. Instead the blood spread over the good Raven's body and got darker and darker until he turned pitch black.

He had changed within his heart, too, for as hard as he tried he could not make a perfect creature. Every creature, including Man, had at least one flaw. Finally, however, he made a creature that was perfect in every way. To his surprise, Fox threatened to kill his perfect creature. "When I compare myself to this perfect creature," Fox explained, "I will only be able to see my imperfections."

Raven thought about what Fox had told him. "With this perfect creature living among my other creatures, no one will notice the perfections in the other creatures—only the imperfections," he thought. He rolled the still-wet creature into a pile of pine needles. Fox tried to take a swipe at the new creature, Porcupine, but Porcupine's needles stuck into unsuspecting Fox. Then something strange happened; from deep within—perhaps from the spirit of his evil brother—Raven felt a new sensation. He laughed for the first time!

62

4. Evaluate Fox's notion that perfection in the creature would cause him only to notice his own imperfections. (AN, E)

_____

_____

_____

_____

_____

_____

_____

5. Make a chart of ten animals noting their perfections and their imperfections. (AP, E)

	Animal	Perfections	Imperfections
1.	_____	_____	_____
2.	_____	_____	_____
3.	_____	_____	_____
4.	_____	_____	_____
5.	_____	_____	_____
6.	_____	_____	_____
7.	_____	_____	_____
8.	_____	_____	_____
9.	_____	_____	_____
10.	_____	_____	_____

6. The idea of a trickster, who is also a creator and/or bringer of culture, is common in North American mythology. Find out who were the trickster figures in each of the following Native American groups: Creek and Cherokee, Cree, Dakota, and Navajo. Create a poster entitled "Tricksters of Native American Mythology." (K, AP)

7. Write an original story centered around a trickster figure. (S)

63

Odds 'n Ends

1. Make a diorama of Mt. Olympus. (C, AP)

2. Create an illustrated booklet of a myth for a young child. Be sure to use language that the child can understand. (S)

3. Create a Mythology Word Search. (K)

4. Make a flipbook of mythological monsters. (C, AP)

5. Create a dot-to-dot of a mythological figure. (C, AP)

6. Do an in-depth study of the mythology of the Aztecs, the Incas or the Mayas. Write a report. (C, AP, AN)

7. Write a play based upon a myth of your choice. Tell whom you would like to play each role and why. (S, E)

8. Design a postage stamp to honor your favorite mythological hero or heroine. (S, E)

9. Prepare a radio broadcast that gives an ''on-the-spot'' account of a mythological event. (C, AP, S)

10. Prepare an annotated bibliography of books on the subject of mythology. (C, AP)

11. Research the mythology of your ancestors. Write a summary of one of the myths you learn about and illustrate it. (C, AP)

12. Pretend that you live in ancient times. There has just been an eclipse of the sun. Write a myth to explain the occurrence. (S)

13. Make a mythology mobile to decorate the room. (K)

14. Draw a detailed picture of a mythological scene on cardboard. Make it into a jigsaw puzzle. (C, AP)

15. Invent a myth to explain hailstones. (S)

Pre-Test

Circle the correct answer.

1. The *Iliad* and the *Odyssey,* important sources of Greek mythology, were written by _____.

      A. Ovid   B. Homer   C. Odysseus   D. Herodotus

2. The most important Greek gods and goddesses lived here.

      A. Mt. Olympus   B. Crete   C. Athens   D. Marathon

3. _____ was the supreme ruler of the Greek gods.

      A. Hades   B. Zeus   C. Ares   D. Athene

4. _____ had to perform twelve labors to win his freedom.

      A. Odysseus   B. Jason   C. Atlas   D. Heracles

5. The Roman equivalent of Aphrodite was _____.

      A. Venus   B. Ceres   C. Juno   D. Diana

6. The _____ was a small wooden image of the goddess Athene (Minerva).

      A. Obelisk   B. Palladium   C. Sphinx   D. Phoenix

7. The greatest sources of Norse mythology were the _____.

      A. Eddas   B. Vedas   C. *Iliad* and the *Odyssey*   D. Poems of Ovid

8. _____, greatest of the Norse gods, was god of war, wisdom, poetry, prophecy, and magic.

      A. Thor   B. Loki   C. Odin   D. Balder

9. _____, god of the sun, became the supreme god of Egypt.

      A. Nut   B. Re   C. Osiris   D. Geb

10. The three gods of the Hindu trinity were all manifestations of one god, _____.

      A. Brahm   B. Vishnu   C. Siva   D. Varuna

Mythology of the Ancient Greeks:
Gods and Goddesses

1. The most powerful gods of the ancient Greeks was _____.

2. The most important gods and goddesses in the mythology of the ancient Greeks lived on _____.

3. _____ is credited with having written the *Iliad* and the *Odyssey*.

4. According to the ancient Greeks, in the beginning there was only a confused, shapeless mass, called _____.

5. Zeus's brother _____ was given control over the elements of water.

6. _____ and Poseidon vied for authority over Attica; _____ won.

7. _____ was the god who had control of the region below the earth. His wife was _____.

8. _____ was the god of fire and those industries dependent upon fire.

9. Many Greeks consulted the _____ to hear her prophecies.

10. Paris's choice of Aphrodite as the fairest and the fulfillment of her promise to him was the legendary cause of _____.

Mythology of the Ancient Greeks:
Lesser Divinities

1. _____ was the demigod who gave the gift of fire to humankind.

2. _____ set loose the evils of the world when she opened the box.

3. _____ was the hero who had twelve labors, or tasks, to perform in order to claim his freedom.

4. _____ were female spirits somewhere between gods and humans. They represented the various features of nature.

5. _____ was punished by Hera by being able only to repeat what was said to her.

6. _____ fell in love with his own image.

7. Nemesis was the goddess of _____.

Roman Mythology

1. The _____ had the responsibility of feeding the sacred flame of Vesta's temple.

2. _____ and _____ were protective household deities.

3. _____ was the god of gates and doorways. He had two faces.

4. _____ was Athene's Roman counterpart.

5. _____ was turned into a spider as a result of her challenge to Minerva.

6. _____ was the Roman god of war.

7. With the touch of his arrow, _____ could cause one to fall in love.

8. _____ was the beautiful maiden who married Cupid and who finally won immortality.

Norse Mythology

1. *Norse* pertains to ancient _____.

2. The greatest sources of Norse mythology are from the two collections of verses known as the_____.

3. The middle world in Norse mythology is called _____.

4. _____ was the home of the Norse gods.

5. The Norse gods were headed by _____.

6. The gods of Norse mythology are collectively known as the _____.

7. _____ was the hall of Odin and the heavenly residence of slain heroes.

8. The _____ were warlike maidens who selected the slain heroes to reside in the heavenly residence.

9. Thor, son of Odin, had three sacred objects: a belt, iron gloves, and _____.

10. _____ the Good, the shining god, was the most beloved of all the Norse gods. His death was indirectly caused by Loki.

Egyptian Mythology

1. Originally, Egyptian gods were pictured as _____.

2. _____, the sun god, became the supreme god of all Egypt.

3. _____ was the god of Thebes. His priests worked hard to get people to identify him with the sun god.

4. _____ was the sky goddess.

5. _____ was the kindest of the gods. He was murdered by his evil brother Set (Seth).

6. _____, whose symbol was an ostrich feather, stood for truth, justice, and order.

7. _____ was the bull of Memphis.

8. A ninefold divinity is called an _____.

9. To preserve the bodies of pharaohs and other important people, a system of embalming and drying, called _____, was practiced.

10. A pyramid was actually a _____.

The Mythologies of India, China, and Japan

India

1. The oldest sacred writings of the Hindus are the _____.

2. The three chief gods of the later Hindu religion are actually three manifestations of one supreme being, _____.

3. According to Hindu mythology, it was _____'s job to preserve the world.

4. According to Hindu mythology, it was _____'s job to destroy the world.

China

5. The two opposing forces of the Great Unity are _____ and _____.

6. _____ was born of the egg of Chaos. When he died, the four cardinal directions grew from his body.

7. _____ was the great hero who reduced the flood waters.

Japan

8. _____ is the religion indigenous to Japan.

9. _____ is the goddess of the sun. Her brother is Susa-no-o.

10. The two deities sent down from the High Plain of Heaven to create the world were _____, a male, and _____, a female.

The Mythologies of Africa, Polynesia, and North America

Africa

1. The _____ is a symbol of eternity, possibly because it sheds its skin and grows another.

Polynesia

2. According to a Tahitian myth, the god _____ existed from the beginning. He floated upon the water in his canoe and eventually dug up the land.

3. The ancient Hawaiians used the myth of the goddess Pele to explain _____.

North America

4. Many Pueblo tribes believed in _____ spirits who could bring rain, sunshine, and a good harvest.

5. The _____ is an important trickster in the mythology of the native people of the Northwest Coast.

Post-Test

Circle the correct answer.

1. This important source of Greek mythology was written by Homer.

    A. *Metamorphoses*   B. the Vedas   C. the *Iliad*   D. the Eddas

2. _____ was seized by Hades to become his queen.

    A. Persephone   B. Echo   C. Hera   D. Athene

3. _____ gave the gift of fire to humankind.

    A. Heracles   B. Prometheus   C. Odysseus   D. Paris

4. The judgment of Paris led to (the) _____.

    A. Trojan War   B. Persian War   C. Ragnarök   D. Creation of the World

5. _____ was the greatest of the Norse gods.

    A. Re   B. Zeus   C. Odin   D. Brahm

6. _____ stood for truth, justice, and order.

    A. Maat   B. Scarab   C. Apis   D. Sphinx

7. The two opposing forces in Chinese mythology are called _____ and _____.

    A. Koji-ki/Nihon-gi   B. Isis/Osiris   C. Mudheads/Koshare   D. Ying/Yang

8. The oldest writings of the Hindus are called the _____.

    A. Eddas   B. Vedas   C. Shinto   D. Volsunga Saga

9. According to Japanese mythology, _____ created the world.

    A. Izanagi and Izanami   B. Ama-Terasu   C. Susa-no-o   D. Tengu

10. This animal often represents eternity in African mythology.

    A. Chameleon   B. Dog   C. Snake   D. Rabbit

Mythology
Crossword Puzzle

Across

4. His oracle was at Delphi.
6. Son of Odin; killed with mistletoe.
9. Mischievous giant of Norse mythology.
11. Greek goddess of beauty.
12. Egyptian principal of truth, justice, and order.
13. A narrative poem.
17. Messenger to the Greek gods.
19. Greek hero who had to perform twelve tasks.
20. Where Jupiter was the supreme god.
22. This Greek god of flocks and shepherds was part goat.
23. Home of the Norse gods.
25. Most beneficent of the Egyptian gods.
26. Mjollnir was this Norse god's weapon.
28. This goddess of the rainbow was Hera's messenger.
29. The nine-fold divinity of the Egyptians, for example.
31. Zeus's brother who controlled the ocean.
35. Greek god who ruled the underworld.
37. Son of Daedalus; he flew too near the sun.
38. Same as 12 across.
40. Sea-nymphs; their singing charmed mariners to leap into the sea.
42. Hawaiian goddess of volcanoes.
44. Pertaining to ancient Scandinavia.

Down

1. Original meaning of *psyche*.
2. Hall of Odin; heavenly residence of slain heroes.
3. Deities of the Roman household; souls of dead ancestors.
5. His *Metamorphoses* is an important source of Roman mythology.
7. Persephone's mother.
8. What the Trojan Horse was made of.
10. Where principal Greek gods lived.
14. What Persephone did in Hades to require her to return.
15. Wife of Zeus.
16. Principal god of Greek pantheon.
18. Relationship of Cupid to Venus.
19. Same as 15 down.
21. What Prometheus gave to humankind.
23. Greek god of war.
24. Raven was one.
25. Norse god of wisdom, war, art, culture, and the dead.
27. The only thing to remain in Pandora's box.
30. Athene turned her into a spider.
32. In Egyptian mythology, the wife of Osiris.
33. He fell in love with his image.
34. Ancient Roman god of gates and doorways.
36. Helios was this kind of god.
39. The sun god, supreme deity of ancient Egypt (variant spelling).
41. Nymph who faded to nothing but a voice.
43. Same as 39 down.

74

Answers to Tests, Quizzes, and Crossword Puzzle

Pre-Test

1. B	6. B
2. A	7. A
3. B	8. C
4. D	9. B
5. A	10. A

Quiz After Page 19

1. Zeus
2. Mt. Olympus
3. Homer
4. Chaos
5. Poseidon
6. Athene; Athene
7. Hades; Persephone
8. Hephaestus
9. Oracle (Delphic Oracle)
10. The Trojan War

Quiz After Page 26

1. Prometheus
2. Pandora
3. Heracles
4. Nymphs
5. Echo
6. Narcissus
7. Vengeance

Quiz After Page 30

1. Vestal Virgins
2. Lares and Penates
3. Janus
4. Minerva
5. Arachne
6. Mars
7. Cupid
8. Psyche

Quiz After Page 45

1. Scandinavia
2. Eddas
3. Midgard
4. Asgard
5. Odin
6. Aesir
7. Valhalla
8. Valkyries
9. His hammer (Mjollnir)
10. Balder (Baldr)

1. Animals
2. Ra (Re)
3. Amun (Ammon, Amon, Amen, etc.)
4. Nut
5. Osiris
6. Maat
7. Apis
8. Ennead
9. Mummification
10. Tomb

Quiz After Page 56

1. Vedas
2. Brahm
3. Vishnu
4. Shiva (Siva)
5. Yin and Yang
6. Pan-ku
7. Yü
8. Shinto
9. Ama-Terasu
10. Izanagi; Izanami

Quiz After Page 63

1. Snake
2. Tiki
3. Volcanoes
4. Kachina
5. Raven

Post-Test

1. C	6. A
2. A	7. D
3. B	8. B
4. A	9. A
5. C	10. C

Answers to Crossword Puzzle

```
        S              V              L
    A P O L L O        A        B A L D E R
        U     V        L   W        E
        L O K I   A P H R O D I T E   M A A T
        L     D        A   O        S
        Y       B A L L A D        T       H
        M       T     L   Z      H E R M E S
        P     H E R A C L E S        R     R O M E
        U     E        U   F        P A N
    A S G A R D   T   O S I R I S
T H O R     A     R   D        R
    O   E         I R I S      E N N E A D
    P O S E I D O N C   N              R
    E       S     A   J        H A D E S
        I C A R U S   M A A T        C   U
        S     C   T     N          H   N
              I   E     U          H   R
              S I R E N S        P E L E
              S           C
              U     H     R
              S   N O R S E
```

Glossary

augury—the art of foretelling events by observing and interpreting signs and omens, especially in ancient Rome.

cosmognony—a theory or model of the evolution of the universe.

culture hero—a mythological hero who, although not necessarily responsible for creation, made the world fit for human life.

demigod—a being of partly divine origin and godlike in form; associated with the creation of humankind and the earliest incidents of civilization, especially in ancient Greece.

ennead—a set of nine; for example, a nine-fold divinity.

epic—an extended narrative poem celebrating the feats of a legendary or traditional hero.

fable—a legendary story of supernatural happenings often meant to teach a lesson; made up by an individual.

myth—a story of anonymous origin constructed by generations of people as an interpretation of natural events. The events surpass the ordinary world and include gods, demigods, and other extraordinary beings.

mythographer—a recorder or narrator of myths.

mythology—a collection of myths about the origin and history of a people and their deities, ancestors, and heroes.

nymph—one of numerous female spirits in Greek and Roman mythology inhabiting and representing features of nature, such as woodlands and water.

oracle—a shrine consecrated to the worship and consultation of a prophetic god; a person who transmits the prophecies from a deity at such as shrine.

pantheon—all the gods of a people.

trickster—one who plays tricks; a mischievous animal-god found in many North American Indian myths.

trinity—a group of three closely related members, especially of three divine figures.

Answers and Background Information to Activities

WHAT IS MYTHOLOGY? (pages 5-6)

1. The Latin word *fabula* originally had a similar meaning to that of the Greek *muthos;* it denoted "word," in the sense of a final pronouncement. Both "myth" and "fable," however, have come to mean a fictitious or untrue story. True myths, however, are not presented as fictitious. No attempt is made to prove or justify the extraordinary events in myths because "myth" is a form of religious symbolization.

A fable is a story made up by an individual. The characters and plot are made up; the author does not expect the readers to believe that either are real. Rather, the author merely uses the story as the vehicle for moral or didactic instruction.

A myth, on the other hand, is of anonymous origin. It is constructed by generations of people as an interpretation of natural events. Although no attempt is made to prove the events, the events are accepted by the people as true.

3. Students should include the following facts: The accounts are presented with an implied authority. The events surpass the ordinary world but are, nevertheless, basic to that world. The time is usually inconceivably long ago. Some characters, at least, are not ordinary beings but are gods, demigods, or other extraordinary beings.

4. The Abnaki myth tells of a lonely man who meets a beautiful woman with long, silky blond hair. She promises to be with him always if he follows her instructions. He makes a fire and drags her over the burned ground as she instructed. In time a corn stalk appears, and he sees her silken hair. Whenever the Abnaki see the silken hair of the corn, they know the beautiful woman is still with them to keep them from being lonely.

5. Paul Tilliach (1886-1965), a theologian, and philosphers Karl Jaspers (1883-1969) and G. Gusdorf were among those to argue that there is a mythological dimension to science.

6. Students might be given a list of poets and authors to research. Some suggestions are George Byron, William Cowper, John Dryden, John Keats, Henry Wadsworth Longfellow, John Milton, Thomas Moore, Alexander Pope, William Shakespeare, Percy Bysshe Shelley, and Alfred Tennyson.

8. Before the introduction of writing, myths were preserved in the oral traditions: the sacred ceremonials of priests and the narratives chanted by minstrels and by professional bards who wandered from village to village. Most of what we know today about the mythology of these ancient cultures comes from a few important sources.

Sources of Greek Mythology

One of the most important sources of knowledge about Greek mythology is Homer. Homer, who is credited with writing the *Iliad* and the *Odyssey,* is almost as great a mythical figure as the heroes of his great works. Seven towns vie for recognition as his place of birth. Homer is believed to have been a wandering minstrel who travelled from place to place, visiting both humble cottages and royal courts alike. According to the Greek historian Herodotus, Homer was born in 850 B.C.

Another important source of Greek mythology is Hesiod, an eighth-century B.C. Greek poet. His two great poems were the *Works and Days* and the *Theogony.* From the *Theogony* we learn the Greek mythology of the creation of the world and the family of the gods, including their wars and their attitudes toward humankind.

Another source of our information are the lyric poets of the seventh and sixth centuries B.C., such as Pindar, Alcaeus, Sappho, and Simonides. Pindar, who lived from about 522 to 433 B.C., was one of the greatest lyric poets of Greece. Not only did he write hymns and songs to praise the gods, he also composed odes to honor the victors in the national athletic contests. In them he used the mythical exploits of Greek heroes as a text from which to draw the appropriate morals.

The three great tragic poets of Greece—Aeschylus, Sophocles, and Euripides—also provide us with much information. From Aeschylus (525-456 B.C.) we learn about the fortunes of Prometheus. From Sophocles (c. 496-406 B.C.) we learn more about the family of Agamemnon, the myths of Oedipus, the Trojan War, and the death of Heracles. From Euripides (c. 480-406 B.C.), seventeen of whose dramas remain, we get stories of Agamemnon's daughters, of Alcestis, and of the adventures of Media. The comedies of Aristophanes (c. 448-380 B.C.) are also an important source of knowledge.

Of course, it is not just the poets who provide us with information about the mythology of the ancient Greeks. Historians such as Lucian, Pausanias, and above all, Herodotus also serve as important sources. Herodotus, who lived in the fifth century B.C., is called the "Father of History." He incorporated many myths into his accounts of the conflicts between Greeks and Asians.

Sources of Roman Mythology

As in Greek mythology, the works of the poets were the most important means of preservation of Roman myths. Virgil, born in Mantua in 70 B.C., was one of the great poets of the Age of Augustus. His great epic the *Aeneid,* which tells the story of the mythical hero Aeneas, is ranked next to Homer's epics by scholars, although many consider it inferior to Homer's works in terms of originality.

It is from Ovid's *Metamorphoses* that we have taken most of our stories of Greek and Roman mythology. Also known as Naso, Ovid lived from 43 B.C. to A.D. 18. The works of other poets, such as Horace, also added to our knowledge. So did the tragedies of Seneca, who based his plays on such legends as Cupid and Psyche.

© **1994 Educational Impressions, Inc.**

Sources of Norse Mythology

Norsemen were those people who inhabited the lands which are now known as Sweden, Denmark, Norway, and Iceland. Their mythology has been preserved for us through many runes, the Skaldic poems, the Sagas, and the Eddas.

The earliest runes were merely fanciful signs believed to have mysterious powers. Later on the term came to mean the letters of the alphabet. Occasionally, the name of one or another god was named in the runes.

The Skaldic poems were the poems of the bards (singing poets) and the poets of Scandinavia. The Skalds told of the exploits of heroes, living and dead, and were accompanied by music and poetry. The Skaldic verse forms are thought to have been devised in Norway in the ninth century. The syllables and lines were strictly counted and the forms of the endings carefully chosen. There was also a great deal of alliteration, internal rhyme, and consonance. The stanzas usually consisted of two one-half stanzas of four lines each. Our greatest source of Norse mythology has been the Eddas. The Eddas refer to two collections of verse, although it is not clear what the original term meant. Unlike the Skaldic verse, the Eddaic verse was mostly composed in free alliterative measures.

The manuscript known as the *Elder Edda,* or *Poetic Edda,* was written down in Iceland about A.D. 1270, but contains material much older than that. In it are several lays, or ballads, with stories about the beginning of the world, the history of the gods, and the end of the pagan world. It is from the *Elder Edda* that we obtained much of our knowledge about Norse mythology.

Even after the Icelanders were converted to Christianity, much of the ancient poetry survived. The Icelanders of the twelfth and thirteenth centuries were among the most learned and most widely travelled people in Europe. In the thirteenth century, there was a renewed interest in the practices of their pagan ancestors. Among the most famous of these antiquarians was Snorri Sturluson. One of his earliest works—and the one for which he is most remembered—was his *Prose Edda,* or *Younger Edda,* written about 1220. Actually, the term ''Edda'' began with this book and was later applied to the *Elder Edda.*

The *Prose Edda* began with a poem which was in reality a manual of Icelandic poetry. First Sturluson exemplified 102 kinds of verse; then he described the speech of the Skalds and their allusions to ancient gods and heroes. In the last section he described all the major Norse deities and their functions.

Sources of German Mythology

German myths have been preserved for us in the German folk songs and in the *Nibelungenlied,* or *Lay* (Ballad) *of the Nibelungs,* which is an outgrowth of the songs. The story of the Volsungs and the Nibelungs is common to both the Norse and the German mythologies, each with a different version.

Sources of Oriental Mythology

Egyption records have been preserved for us by means of hieroglyphics, sacred papyri, and *The Book of the Dead and of the Lower Hemisphere.* Indian records have been saved in the Holy Scriptures of the Hindus, known as the Vedas. Much information has also been passed on to us by means of the two great Indian epics: the *Mahâbharâta* and the *Ramayana. The Mahâbharâta (The Great Feud of the Bhâratas)* is a storehouse of Indian myth. The *Râmâyana* is supposed to have been written by the poet Vâlmîki. It tells how Prince Rama rescues his lovely wife, who has been stolen by the king of the demons. Persian (Iranian) records have been preserved in the sacred book of the ancient Persians, called the *Avesta.*

81

MYTHOLOGY OF THE ANCIENT GREEKS (pages 7-26)
Sources of Greek Mythology (pages 7-9)

1. Some people believe that poems of such length could not have been committed to writing at so early an age as that usually ascribed to the *Iliad* and the *Odyssey:* an age earlier than the date of any remaining inscriptions and when no materials capable of containing such long productions were yet introduced into use. They ask how poems of such length could have been handed down from age to age by means of memory alone. This can be explained by the fact that professionals (Rhapsodists) were trained and paid to memorize and rehearse the national legends.

Most scholars believe that the framework and much of the structure belong to Homer, but that there are many interpolations and additions by others.

2. The seven cities which claimed to be the birthplace of Homer are Smyra, Scio, Rhodes, Colophon, Salamis, Argos, and Athens.

4. Danae and Perseus were found and cared for by a kindly fisherman. Perseus grew to be strong and brave. After a series of exploits, including cutting off the head of the Gorgon Medusa, Perseus found himself at the games being held in Larissa. When it was his turn to throw the discus, a terrible thing happened. It went out of control and landed in the stands, killing one of the spectators—King Acrisius.

5. Uranus was both the son and the husband of Gaea. His many children included the twelve Titans, the three one-eyed monsters called the Cyclops, and the three 100-handed giants called the Hecatoncheires. Uranus cast the Cyclops and the Hecatoncheires back into the earth as soon as they were born. Gaea, however, rebelled at her husband's treatment of her children—however unusual they might be. She encouraged her Titan sons to rebel against their father. Uranus had them thrown into Tartarus, where he kept them bound. Gaea then gave a sickle to Cronus, the youngest Titan, and told him how to use it against Uranus. The Titans were freed and Cronus held the supreme position.

According to a prophecy of his parents, Cronus, too, would be destroyed by one of his children; therefore, he swallowed his children as they were born. His wife, Rhea, however, substituted a stone for their last child, Zeus. Zeus was taken to Crete and hidden in a cave on Mt. Ida. When grown, he came back and gave Cronus a potion, causing him to bring back his three sisters and two brothers.

A long struggle against the Titans followed, but finally Zeus established his right to reign in place of his father Cronus.

6. The Naiades were nymphs of fountains and lived in and near fountains and springs. The Oreades were mountain nymphs and lived on mountains and hills. The Dryades were nymphs of trees and, therefore, lived in the forests.

7.

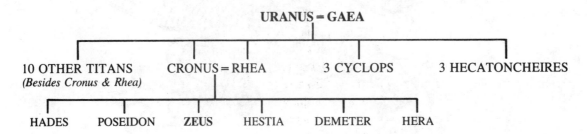

Zeus and the Gods of Mt. Olympus (page 11)

1. Zeus: Supreme ruler of gods, heavens, earth, and air
   Hera: Queen of gods
   Hades: Underworld
   Poseidon: Ocean
   Demeter: Agriculture
   Apollo: Archery, prophecy, music
   Artemis: Moon, the chase (hunt)
   Hephaestus: Fire, metal-working, pottery
   Athene: Wisdom
   Ares: War
   Aphrodite: Love, beauty
   Hermes: Messenger of the gods; commerce, skill, science
   Hestia: Hearth

Zeus's Brothers (pages 12-13)

1. Poseidon was worshipped most zealously in the seaport towns, for it was there that they were in most need of his favor.

2. With a stroke of his trident, Poseidon caused a salty spring to well up on the Acropolis of Athens. The 400-foot high rock was previously without water. Athene caused the first olive tree to grow from the same bare rock. It was deemed the greatest gift that could be bestowed, and Athene was granted sovereignty of the land. Poseidon reacted by spitefully flooding the land.

3. The Underworld was conceived as a source of treasures. The growth of vegetation was seen to be steadily pushed upward by a divine force below. Also, the metals most precious to humankind could only be found by digging into that dark region. By virtue of his powers in these regards, Hades was viewed as a true friend of humankind. On the other hand, as the monarch of the dark realm inhabited by the shades of the dead, Hades was a god to be feared.

4. The Greeks believed that the seeds of their crops were, like the dead, buried in the earth in the parched summer months before the autumn sowing. Like Persephone, they came up again and stayed until it was again time for them to return underground.

The Artist God (page 13)

1. Some of the famous works made by Hephaestus were Zeus's aegis and sceptre, the armor of Achilles and Memmon, Hera's throne, the net in which he caught Aphrodite and Ares, and Athene's shield.

2. Hephaestus is the personification of the fire that burnt forth as a volcanic eruption. The word "volcano" comes from his Roman name, Vulcan.

A Foolhardy Request: Phaethon's Downfall (pages 14-15)

5. Icarus was the son of Daedalus, the skillful inventor who had build the Labyrinth in Crete for King Minos. Daedalus incurred the wrath of Minos when he helped Theseus escape from the Labyrinth. Daedalus, however, made wings with which he and his son could escape. Daedalus warned Icarus to fly straight and to follow him all the way. If he flew too low, the water of the sea would make the wings too heavy; if he flew too high, the sun would melt the wax. Daedalus was sure his son would obey, but he was wrong. Icarus became overconfident and soared towards the blazing sun. His wings melted, and he fell into the sea. Daedalus could do nothing but grieve as he watched his son plunge to his death.

The Judgment of Paris (pages 17-19)

1. Helen was called the face that launched a thousand ships for her role in instigating of the Trojan War.

4. At Odysseus's suggestion, the Greeks constructed an immense Wooden Horse in which Odysseus and twenty-nine other armed Greeks hid. Except for a man named Sinon, the Greeks pretended to sail away. Sinon pretended to be a Greek traitor. He told the Trojans, who had come to see the horse, that whichever city contained the horse could not be conquered. Laocoon warned his countrymen against accepting this gift, but they did not listen. It is from this episode that we get the saying "Beware of Greeks bearing gifts."

Prometheus and the Gift of Fire (pages 21-23)

3. Heracles was the man destined to free Prometheus and save the gods. Heracles was in the process of carrying out the twelve labours imposed upon him by King Eurystheus. The eleventh labour, or task, was to fetch the golden apples which had been given as a wedding gift by Gaea to Hera. They were in the keeping of the Hesperides. Prometheus advised Heracles to send Atlas, father of the Hesperides, to bring him the apples. In order to carry out the task, however, Heracles had to hold up the heavens for Atlas. Atlas brought back the apples and tried to trick Heracles into holding the heavens forever by offering to take the apples to Eurystheus himself; however, Heracles was too clever. He asked Atlas to hold the heavens for a moment as he made himself more comfortable. As soon as the heavens were safe, Heracles hurried away with the apples.

The Twelve Labours of Heracles (page 24)

1. The twleve labours, or tasks, were as follows:
   Bring back the skin of the Nemean Lion
   Slaughter the Hydra
   Bring back Artemis's beautiful hind with golden antlers
   Catch the Erymanthian Boar
   Cleanse the stables of King Augeas
   Get rid of the Stymphalian Birds
   Capture the Cretan Bull
   Fetch the man-eating mares of Diomedes
   Obtain the girdle, or belt, of Hippolyta, queen of the Amazons
   Steal the cattle of the three-headed ogre Geryon
   Bring back the golden apples of the Hesperides
   Bring back Cerberus, the Hound of Hades

Echo and Narcissus (pages 25-26)

3. Echo: The repetition of a sound by reflection of sound waves from a surface.

Narcissism: Excessive love or admiration of oneself.

Nemesis: One who inflicts retribution or vengeance; an unbeatable rival.

ROMAN MYTHOLOGY (pages 27-30)

1. The accredited Roman equivalents of the deities are as follows:

Zeus: Jupiter, Jove
Hera: Juno
Apollo: Apollo
Artemis: Diana
Athene: Minerva
Aphrodite: Venus
Demeter: Ceres
Hestia: Vesta
Hephaestus: Vulcan
Ares: Mars
Hermes: Mercury
Poseidon: Neptune
Dionysus: Bacchus

2. Beginning with the third century, Roman aristocrats were given a Greek education. It finally reached a point where nearly every phase of Rome's intellectual life was influenced by the Greeks. The Greeks were imitated in literature, philosophy, and the arts. In fact, some went to such an extreme to copy the Greek models that other Romans, wanting to preserve their own traditions, tried unsuccessfully to check the spread of Greek culture.

Protectors of the Household (page 28)

1. The sacred flame could only be rekindled by holding a glass up to the rays of the sun.

2. As the porter of heaven, Janus opened and closed all things. Janus, therefore, was the god of a "good beginning." Even when Jupiter was conceived as consenting to an enterprise, Janus was believed to have control of the prosperity in carrying it out, for the Romans laid great stress on the circumstances of the commencement of a project. The Roman poet Ovid had Janus say, "Everything depends on the beginning."

3. The Penates guarded the pantry.

4. The Lares, or Lars, were deified spirits of mortals. They were believed to be souls of the ancestors, who watched over and protected their descendents.

Minerva (page 29)

1.

The Palladium, a small wooden image of the goddess Athene (Minerva), was believed to have fallen from heaven, thereupon becoming the property of Troy. As long as the Trojans had possession of the Palladium, their city would be safe; however, during the Trojan War, Diomedes, and Odysseus stole the statue, and the Greeks proceeded to capture the city by means of the Wooden Horse. Later on, other cities—for example, Argos, Athens, and Rome—claimed possession of it. It was firmly believed that the safety of the city depended upon that possession.

2. Arachne was an excellent weaver. She was so good that people thought Minerva herself had taught her; however, Arachne was too vain regarding her skill to bear to be thought a pupil of anyone—even a goddess! She challenged the goddess to a contest to compare their work. Minerva disguised herself as an old woman and tried to convince Arachne of her foolishness. Even when she showed herself in her true form, Arachne insisted on proceeding. When Arachne wove scenes representing the loves of the gods and goddesses into her cloth, Minerva became even more angry. Finally, anger turned to rage, and she tore the cloth into shreds. Minerva then touched the forehead of Arachne and made her feel guilt and shame. Arachne was so ashamed, in fact, that she tried to hang herself. Minerva pitied her and decided to let her live; however, she arranged it so Arachne and all her descendents would remember the lesson of that fateful day. She transformed her into a spider.

4. Minerva (Athene) was the goddess of well-matched, chivalrous fights. When fighting, she was invulnerable and always on the side of the victor. It was defensive war that she patronized. Unlike Minerva, Mars (Ares) took pleasure in slaughter and massacre. He was not only the god of battle, but also the personification of war itself. Because in war there is both victory and defeat, Mars was sometimes wounded and even taken prisoner. Although Ares was worshipped in Greece, it was in Rome, with its conquests and pride in military power, that the god of war received the most zealous worship. Mars was second only to Jupiter as the guardian of the state. In fact, the Romans believed themselves descendents of Mars, based upon their belief that Mars was father to Romulus and Remus.

Cupid and Psyche (page 30)

1. Poets have compared the soul to the way in which a butterfly frees itself from its chrysalis, rises on wing, and floats in the light.

2. There will be many answers, but perhaps Psyche should have pointed out that if he had trusted her, he would have let her know who he was.

NORSE AND GERMANIC MYTHOLOGY (page 31-45)

1. When the Christian missionaries tried to destroy the paganism of the old Germans, they were quite successful. At the same time as Christianity was spreading over Germany and Scandinavia, an exodus of the Norsemen (as ancient Scandinavians were called) was also taking place. The exodus resulted in the colonization of Iceland—then called Snowland—in the middle of the ninth century. There the Vikings established their independent principalities, unbothered by Christian priests. These Icelandic Norsemen looked down upon those who had remained on the continent and who had given up their old traditions for the new. They preserved for five more centuries the old religion of their ancestors. Although Christianity was practiced in Iceland, there seems to have been less friction between the old Odinism and the new Christianity in Iceland than elsewhere. Even after most of the Icelanders had been converted, much of their ancient poetry survived. In the thirteenth century, there seems to have been an antiquarian revival in the interest of the pagan practices of their ancestors.

2.

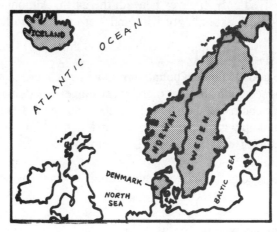

The Creation (page 32)

1. Midgard was midway between Muspelheim and Niflheim.

2. The three huge roots of Yggdrasil stretched to Jötunheim (the home of the giants), to Midgard (the home of the mortals), and below Niflheim to the world of the dead.

Asgard (page 33)

1. The twelve gods of the Aesir are Thor, Baldr, Freyr, Tyr, Bragi, Hodr, Heimdall, Vithar, Vali, Ullr, Ve, and Forseti.

2. Bifrost was the rainbow.

A Somber View of Life (page 34-35)

1. The Olympian gods were immortal and invincible; as they knew they could suffer no harm, they had nothing to fear. The Norse gods, on the other hand, had to constantly fear the dangers of the giants who lived in Jötunheim. In fact, they knew that someday they would be defeated.

2. Mimir insisted that Odin pay for the knowledge by leaving an eye.

4. The luminous bands or streamers of light sometimes seen in the night skies of the northern regions are called the aurora borealis. Scientists believe they are caused by the ejection of charged particles from outer space into the magnetic field of the earth. (In the southern hemisphere it is called the aurora australis.)

5. Odin's popularity spread during the Viking Age. The Vikings were a group of Scandinavian people who plundered the coasts of northern and western Europe. For this reason, Odin became god of Vikings and other lawless men.

Thor (pages 37-38)

2. Thor's chief weapon was Mjollnir, a short-handled hammer which caused thunder as it flew. With it, Thor could smash giants and break mountains. The hammer always returned to his hand like a boomerang.

3. The Elves—both the Black Elves and the Elves of Light—belonged to a class of beings inferior to gods and yet in possession of great power. The Elves of Light, also called white spirits, were brighter than the sun. They wore delicate and transparent garments. These beautiful creatures loved the light and had a close relationship with humans, of whom they generally were fond. These white spirits lived in Alfheim, the land of Freyr, god of the sun. The Black, or Night, Elves were different creatures altogether. They were dirty-looking, ugly, long-nosed dwarfs. Unlike the Elves of Light who always appeared in the sunlight, these creatures avoided the sun at all costs, for the sun beams would turn them into stone. These dwarfs lived only in caves beneath the earth. Although the white spirits were more beautiful, the Night Elves were exceedingly wise and were expert craftsmen.

The Death of Balder (pages 39-41)

1. Loki was seized by the gods, who then bound him in a deep cavern. They placed a serpent above his head so that its venom dripped upon his face, thereby causing excruciating pain. Loki's wife Sigyn came to his aid and caught the venom in a cup as it fell; however, each time the cup was full, she had to remove the cup in order to empty it. Although the venom touched him only briefly, his pain was so great that the ground shook, causing what we now call an earthquake.

3. Sleipner was an eight-legged green stallion which could outrun the wind. It had been given to Odin by Loki.

5. Frigga decreed that anyone who passed beneath this plant would receive a kiss of love.

6. The mistletoe is a parasitic shrub. It grows and feeds on the branches of other trees but contributes nothing to the survival of its host.

The Tale of the Volsungs and the Nibelungs (pages 42-44)

1. The tetralogy is called the *Ring of the Nibelung*. The four operas are *Rhine-gold,* the *Valkyrie,* the *Siegfried,* and the *Twilight (or Dusk) of the Gods.*

4. Atli represents Attila, leader of the Huns. The Huns were a fierce, barbaric race of Asian nomads who ravaged Europe in the fourth and fifth centuries A.D.

5. The "golden treasure" probably represents the sunlight.

Goddesses' Rights (page 45)

Only two goddesses in Norse mythology are really notable: Frigga and Freyja. Frigga, the wife of Odin and mother of Balder, controlled nature. Although very wise, she kept what she knew to herself. Freyja was the goddess of love and fertility. She was also the goddess of wealth, as represented by her ownership of the Brising necklace, forged by dwarfs, and her tears of gold. Freyja also had some qualities of a death goddess; she rode to the battlefield and claimed the dead not taken by the Valkyries.

The only realm handed over to the rule of a goddess was Niflheim, the Kingdom of Death. It was given to Hel by Odin.

EGYPTIAN MYTHOLOGY (pages 46-50)

1. Egypt had widely scattered centers of culture; each of these centers contributed its own elements to Egyptian mythology. Also, the fact that Egyptian civilization flourished for more than 3,000 years added to the probability that changes would occur.

Ra (page 47)

1. The Greek counterpart to Ra, or Re, was Helios. Helios was the god of the sun. His sisters were Selene, the moon, and Eos, the dawn. Helios rose each morning in his gold horse-driven chariot until evening, when he sank into the west. Helios was the god who sees and hears everything. He was young and handsome and had bright, shining eyes. Helios had twelve palaces, each of which corresponded to a different sign of the Zodiac. It was believed that he rotated from palace to palace during the course of the year.

2 The scarab is a type of beetle, regarded as sacred by the ancient Egyptians. Sculptures of the scarab were used as talismans (objects marked with magical signs and believed to confer on their bearers supernatural powers or protection) and as symbols of the soul.

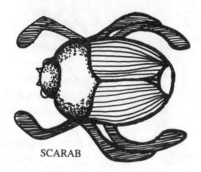

SCARAB

3. The more power the god had, the more power the priests would have. When Thebes became the capital, Amun's importance grew. By the time of the New Kingdom, Amun had become king of the gods and magnificent temples were erected at Karnak in his honor.

The Creation (page 48)

1. According to Heliopolitan theology, Ra (Re) was the first god. From him, in a manner resembling a sneeze, came Shu (air), and Tefnet (moisture). Shu and Tefnet were parents to Geb and Nut. Geb and Nut gave birth to Osiris, Isis, Set, and Nephthys.

2. During the Fifth Dynasty, the theology of Heliopolis—the ennead—became the official theology. The kings of the period used the title "Son of Re." According to legend, the first three kings of this dynasty were sons of the god Re himself. From the Fifth Dynasty on, Son of Re became a regular part of a king's title. There was now undoubted predominance of the god Re.

3. Shu, as the god of air, caused a great wind to life Nut's star-covered body. Shu then became the air between Nut, the star-covered sky, and Geb, the earth. Every day Re, the sun, traveled across the area of Nut's body. At night the goddess Nut came down to her husband Geb, causing darkness.

Osiris (page 49)

1. According to one myth, Isis and Horus hunted for the pieces until they had found them all. The rites and prayers that they conducted, with the aid of Nephthys, Thoth, and Anubis, caused the pieces of the body to join and become whole. Isis then used a magic formula to bring him back to life.

According to another version, Isis recovered all but one piece of the body and buried them where she found them. Osiris then became judge of the underworld. Horus avenged Osiris's death by temporarily overcoming Set with the help of Thoth (reason).

3. Apis, the bull of Memphis, was worshipped with great reverence. The individual animal that was worshipped as Apis was recognized by certain signs. The animal had to be very black with a white square mark on the forehead, a white mark in the form of an eagle on his back, and a lump under his tongue in the form of a scarab beetle. Once found, the bull was kept in a building facing east; there he was fed with milk for four months. Then, with the new moon, the bull was placed in a beautifully decorated vessel and taken down the Nile to Memphis to a temple with two chapels and an exercise court. He was treated wonderfully—except for one thing: he was only allowed to live for twenty-five years. At that time, if still alive, he was drowned in the sacred cistern and buried in the temple of Serapis. The whole land mourned for the bull until its successor was found.

Mummification (page 50)

1. The pharaohs were the first real kings in the world. Before them, men had ruled over a certain town or tribe. The pharaohs were the first to rule over an entire country. Because they were so powerful, they were able to demand the construction of the magnificent tombs we call the pyramids.

THE MYTHOLOGY OF INDIA (pages 51-52)

1. Sanskrit

2. The principal deities of the Vedas were Dyaus, Prithivi, Varuna, Surya, Savitri, Indra, Agni, Soma, Ushas, Yama and Yami, and Vayr.

3. Agni was created as a result of the rubbing together of two sticks. He then burst forth from the woods in flames. When excited by the wind, he rushed among the trees and consumed the forest. Agni had two faces, three legs, seven tongues, and seven arms. Agni was the god of fire. He personified fire in three forms: the sun, lightning, and sacrificial fire. Agni had two sides to his nature, just as the fire that he personified has two sides to its nature. Fire warms us and cooks our food, but it also destroys our homes and kills the people in them.

4. Brahma, Vishnu, and Siva (Shiva) are the three gods of the Hindu trinity.

90

5.

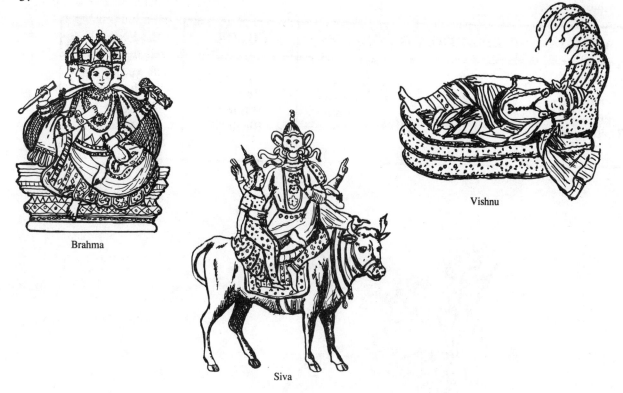

Brahma

Siva

Vishnu

Brahma, the red god, is the creative power of Brahm's energy.
Vishnu, the blue god, is the preserving power of Brahm's energy.
Siva, the white god, is the destroying phase of Brahm's energy.

6. Siva destroyed the world so that it could be re-created. The Hindu belief is that the universe evolves and disappears in cycles.

CHINESE MYTHOLOGY (pages 53-54)

1. According to Chinese mythology, there was at one time a Great Unity. From this Great Unity came two forces. The interaction of these two forces created the visible universe, called the "ten thousand things." Without the opposing forces, we would have no way of perceiving things. For example, without cold, you couldn't perceive hot; without brightness, you couldn't perceive darkness.

After a while, these opposing forces came to be called Yin and Yang. Yin, presented as female, was the dark, quiet, unifying element; Yin was symbolized by such aspects of nature as the earth, the moon, and water. Yang, presented as male, was the bright, active power; Yang was symbolized by the sun, fire, and the sky.

Neither Yin nor Yang is evil. Evil only occurs when there is a lack of harmony between the opposing forces.

 This symbol represents the cosmic theory and came about in later years.

2.

ANIMAL	DIRECTION	SEASON	COLOR	ELEMENT
Dragon	East	Spring	Green	Wood
Phoenix	South	Summer	Red	Fire
Tiger	West	Autumn	White	Metal
Tortoise/Snake	North	Winter	Black	Water

3.

Phoenix

4. A man named Kun stole a piece of magic soil from heaven with which to dam up the waters that covered the land; however, heaven was so enraged by the theft that the harder he worked, the higher the flood waters rose. Kun was executed on Mt. Yü. Three years later, Kun's body was split open and his son, Yü the Great, was brought forth. Yü later managed to dredge the area and reduce the floodwaters. It took him years of strenuous labor to accomplish his task.

5. He received assistance from a variety of spirits and creatures; the most helpful were the tortoise and the dragon. They dragged their tails over the prospective channels in order to provide outlets to the sea. As a result of Yü's work, the world was made suitable for agriculture and habitable for humankind.

7. One day all ten suns appeared in the sky at the same time. The Earth seemed doomed to destruction by their scorching heat. How I, the archer, shot down nine of the suns with his red bow and white arrows.

JAPANESE MYTHOLOGY (pages 55-56)

1. A synonym for *indigenous* is *native*.

2. The sun is represented as female, rather than male. In most religions with a similar worship, the sun is represented as male. Ama-Terasu is the goddess of the sun in Japanese mythology; she is the founder of the royal house of Japan.

3. Ama-Terasu was the goddess of the sun; when she hid in the cave, she deprived the universe of light.

4. In both the story of Ama-Terasu and the story of Demeter, the seasonal barrenness of the land is associated with the grief of the goddess.

5. When the two gods stepped upon the Floating Bridge of Heaven, they noticed something down below. It was the ocean. Izanagi thrust his jeweled spear into the ocean. When he removed the spear, a bit of brine dripped from it and formed an island. They stepped upon it and lived there. The two gods bore the other islands of Japan. They also gave birth to a number of rocks, trees, winds, and mountains.

6. Izanagi escaped from the Ugly Women by trickery. He threw down his comb and then his headdress. The comb turned into bamboo sprouts and headdress into grapes. The Ugly Women stopped to eat the food, providing Izanagi with the opportunity to escape.

7. Tengu are believed to live in trees in the mountains. They live in colonies ruled by a principal tengu who acts as king. The king is served by messenger tengu. Tengu are hybrid creatures—part human and part bird. They are often portrayed as red creatures dressed in cloaks of feathers or leaves and small black hats. Although mischievous in character, they are not truly evil creatures. The tengu are skilled swordsmen and taught the warrior arts to the hero Yoshitsune.

Oni are pink, red, blue, or grey horned devils; most are giants and some have three eyes. Oni have three toes and three fingers. These creatures are cruel, malicious, and stupid.

Kappa are more intelligent than the Oni and not as vicious. The kappa are believed to have taught the skill of bone-setting to humans. Although they have no fur, kappa resemble monkeys. Some have skin; others have fish scales or tortoise shells. These yellow-green creatures are about the size of a ten-year-old human. Their most distinguishing feature is the indentation of the top of the head. The indentation is usually filled with water. When the water spills out, the kappa lose their power. Kappa live in rivers, ponds, and lakes. Their nourishment is derived mainly from horse, cattle, and human blood. They are also fond of cucumbers. It was believed that by throwing cucumbers with the names and ages of family members into the water, the kappa living there would not go after that family. In order to defeat a kappa in battle it is necessary to trick it into lowering its head so that the water spills out. In its weakened state, it can then be forced to make a promise, which it would honor.

93

AFRICAN MYTHOLOGY (pages 57-58)

2. Throughout most of Africa the people are extremely dependent upon rain for survival. Without it, their crops would not grow and they would starve. In the tropics the sun is always present; therefore, although the sun is also vital, there is little need to pray or make sacrifices in order to bring it back.

3. The outer covering of a snake's skin regularly gets replaced. In the first stage, the snake appears cloudy or milky; this is due to a thin layer of fluid which separates the old skin from the new skin beneath it, which is still in the process of forming. When the new skin is completely formed, the next stage begins. The snake will slowly wriggle out of the old skin. It begins at the corner of its lips and turns it inside out as it works off the old skin in one place.

MYTHS OF THE POLYNESIANS (pages 59-60)

1. Polynesia is made up of the scattered islands, roughly between New Zealand, Hawaii, and Easter Island. Among the Polynesians are the Maoris, early inhabitants of New Zealand; the Tahitians; the Samoans; inhabitants of the Carolinas, the Marshalls, and the neighboring islands; and the Hawaiians.

2. Kane shaped and formed two heavens: an Upper Heaven for the gods and goddesses and a Lower Heaven for the Earth he was about to create. He threw up a huge calabash into the air. The top of the calabash became the curved bowl: sky. Two other pieces became the sun and the moon. The seeds, which scattered in the sky, became stars. The rest of the calabash became the Earth, which fell back into the sea. Then he and the other great gods—Kane, Ky, Lono, and Kanaloa—created the animals and plants to live on the Earth. Finally, the gods brought some rich red earth to Kane. He shaped it into man and breathed life into it. Man would be the chief—the ruler of the Earth.

3. The volcanoes of Kauai, Oahu, and Maui are dormant or extinct because Namaki, Sea Goddess, had put out Pele's fires. By the time Pele went to Hawaii, Sea Goddess had realized that she would never be able to kill her. She decided to ignore her and to let her live in Kilauea. That is why Kilauea is the only active volcano of the Hawaiian Islands.

MYTHOLOGY OF NORTH AMERICA (pages 61-63)

1. The Pueblo Indians lived in the arid region of what is now the southwestern part of the United States. The rain gods were more important because the sun needed no encouragement.

2. Snakes were collected from each of the Four Winds (four cardinal points). For nine days the snakes were washed, prayed over, and purified. On the last day they danced together as brothers before being returned to the Four Winds as messengers to the gods. The snakes would implore rain on behalf of the people.

3. Koshare were clowns painted in black and white stripes to represent skeletons.

6. The Creek and Cherokee Trickster was Rabbit, the bringer of fire. The Cree Trickster was Wisagatcah, the creator of the world. The Dakota Trickster was the Moving God, or Wind. The Navajo Trickster was Coyote.

Bibliography

BOOKS

Benardete, Dr. Seth, ed. *Larousse Greek and Roman Mythology*. New York: Mc Graw-Hill Book Company, 1980.

Boase, Wendy. *Ancient Egypt*. New York: Gloucester Press, 1978.

Bowder, Diana, ed. *Who Was Who in the Greek World*. Ithaca, New York: Cornell University Press, 1982.

Bullfinch, Thomas. *A Book of Myths*. New York: Macmillan Publishing Company, 1980.

Coterell, Arthur. *A Dictionary of World Mythology*. New York: G.P. Putnam's Sons, 1980.

Colum, Padraic. *The Golden Fleece*. New York: Macmillan Publishing Company, 1949.

Frazer, James George. *The Golden Bough,* revised. New York: Macmillan Publishing Company, 1950.

Guiarard, Felix, ed. *Larousse Encyclopedia of Mythology*. London: Paul Hamlyn Limited, 1959.

Hamilton, Edith. *Mythology*. Boston: Little, Brown & Company, 1942.

Monaghan, Patricia. *The Book of Goddesses and Heroines*. New York: E.P. Dutton, 1981.

Murray, Alexander Stuart. *Who's Who in Mythology: Classic Guide to the Ancient World*. 1988

Tunis, Edwin. *Indians*. New York: Thomas Y. Crowell, 1979

White, Anne Terry. *A Golden Treasury of Myths and Legends*. New York: Golden Press, 1949.

VIDEOCASSETTES

Timeless Tales: Myths of Ancient Greece, Set I. Hawthorne, New Jersey: January Productions, 1979.

Timeless Tales: Myths of Ancient Greece, Set II. Hawthorne, New Jersey: January Productions, 1986.